"I Don't Know How I Managed to Wait This Long for My Good-Morning Kiss."

Warm breath feathered against her skin. Then his mouth found its target. His lips moved over hers, coaxing, imploring, enticing. The tip of his tongue traced her slightly parted lips, only just penetrating the moistness within, yet the tiny invasion was excruciatingly sensual and explosive. Katy's soft mouth quivered beneath his as fear and pleasure battled for control. She wanted the kiss to end, she wanted it to go on forever. She wanted to wrench herself out of his arms, yet she wanted to melt into him, to never let him go.

GINNA GRAY
admits that for most of her life she has been both an avid reader and a dreamer. For a long time the desire to write, to put her fantasies down on paper, had been growing, until finally she told herself to *do* it. Now, she can't imagine not *writi*

Dear Reader:

I'd like to take this opportunity to thank you for all your support and encouragement of Silhouette Romances.

Many of you write in regularly, telling us what you like best about Silhouette, which authors are your favorites. This is a tremendous help to us as we strive to publish the best contemporary romances possible.

All the romances from Silhouette Books are for you, so enjoy this book and the many stories to come.

Karen Solem
Editor-in-Chief
Silhouette Books

GINNA GRAY
The Gentling

Silhouette *Romance*
Published by Silhouette Books New York
America's Publisher of Contemporary Romance

SILHOUETTE BOOKS, a Division of Simon & Schuster, Inc.
1230 Avenue of the Americas, New York, N.Y. 10020

ISBN: 0-671-57285-7

First Silhouette Books printing March, 1984

10 9 8 7 6 5 4 3 2 1

Map by Ray Lundgren

America's Publisher of Contemporary Romance

Printed in the U.S.A.

To my father, Roy Conn, in loving memory.
He never once doubted that I could do it.

OKLAHOMA

ARK.

NEW MEXICO

Fort Worth ● ● Dallas
● Tyler

LA.

TEXAS

Houston ●
San Antonio ● Galveston ●

MEXICO

GULF OF
MEXICO

TEXAS

Chapter One

Katy Donovan listened to the preacher's pious voice drone on and on, her face a stoic mask. Head unbowed, hands thrust deep inside the pockets of her light, all-weather coat, she stood rigid beside her father, only remotely aware of the biting chill in the March wind or the group of subdued people around her. Overhead, a ragged layer of clouds scudded across the east Texas sky, trailing an eerie pattern of fast moving shadows over the graveside mourners.

It had rained earlier, and the air was heavy with the pungent scents of pine and dank, rusty-red earth. From the woods surrounding the cemetery came the raucous cawing of a flock of crows.

"Dear Lord, we commit unto your keeping the soul of your faithful servant, Henry Alan Barnett," the preacher intoned pontifically. "Henry was a good man, Lord, a respected man. Loved by all, hated by none."

Katy stirred, and at once her father's hand tightened on her arm. On the opposite side of the grave, swathed completely in black and looking tragically beautiful, Saundra Barnett gave a soft cry as she clasped her hands together and lowered her blond head dolorously.

Katy watched her for a moment, then averted her

eyes and stared across the glistening tombstones into the distance. A gusting breeze tore a strand of long black hair from the severe chignon at her nape and whipped it across her pale features. Absently, Katy tucked it back into place.

Suddenly watery sunshine broke through the clouds and glinted off the silver handles of the casket, drawing Katy's unwilling gaze. Her eyes narrowed as a surge of bitterness rose like bile in her throat.

Damn you, Henry Barnett, she screamed silently. May you burn in hell forever! Katy was shaking with the ferocity of her feelings, her pulse throbbing in her throat. Instantly regretting the crack in her composure, she took several deep breaths and forced every sign of anguish from her face.

The young widow stepped forward and placed her hand on the ornate casket. "The Lord giveth and the Lord taketh away," the preacher's sonorous voice chanted. "Blessed be the name of the Lord." With a sob, Saundra turned and flung herself into the arms of the broad-shouldered man at her side.

A grimace of distaste broke the calm mask of Katy's features as she watched the theatrical display. She hadn't noticed the dark-suited man before, and now she wondered who he was. Saundra's latest lover, perhaps? The instant the thought popped into her head, she dismissed it. Not even Saundra would be that brazen. At the moment Katy couldn't see the man clearly. His head was bent over the petite blonde sobbing against his chest, while his hands moved consolingly over her heaving shoulders.

Then, without warning, he looked up. Deep-set hazel eyes locked with Katy's blue ones, and her heart crashed against her ribcage.

Trace! Good Lord! Trace Barnett had come home!

The burning intensity in that boldly familiar look tied Katy's stomach muscles into a hard knot. Shaken, she tore her eyes away and moved closer to her father, grasping his arm for support. Her knees seemed suddenly to have turned to water.

The preacher's voice droned mercifully to a halt, and and his deeply intoned Amen was echoed softly by the cluster of people around the flower-bedecked casket. As he stepped to Saundra's side, Katy turned and began to walk away.

"Katy girl, aren't you going to offer your condolences to the family?"

There was a cold remoteness about her when she turned to face her father, a blankness in the vivid blue eyes that was chilling. "No, Dad. This is as far as I go. I only came to the funeral for your sake."

"Katy, I—" Tom Donovan's voice faltered as a spasm of guilt crossed his craggy features. "I—"

Instantly Katy softened. Placing her hand on his arm, she smiled reassuringly. "Don't worry about it, Dad. I understand. Really I do." She flicked a quick glance in Saundra's direction. "If you want to keep your job at the farm you can't afford to offend the new owner. So go ahead and do whatever you have to. I'll wait for you in the car."

Without another word, she turned and walked away.

The compact car bounced along the twisting, red-dirt road at a fast clip. Through the bare branches overhead Katy could occasionally glimpse the cerulean sky, with its flotilla of puffy clouds. If today's spell of warm weather held, soon even that would not be possible. Within a few weeks the interlacing branches of oaks, elms, sweetgums and pecans would form a leafy canopy over the road.

As she rounded a curve, Katy spied a robin flitting through the trees at the edge of the road. Reacting instinctively, she eased her foot off the accelerator. The reduced speed allowed her gaze to wander briefly from the narrow country lane, and immediately a contented smile curved her mouth.

Signs of spring were all around. Every bare limb was covered with tiny buds. Among the undergrowth, tender pale green shoots were already visible, pushing up through the newly thawed earth and the layers of dead leaves that blanketed the forest floor. Snowy white drifts of flowering dogwood brightened the deepest shadows of the forest, and the pinkish-lavender blossoms of the redbud trees provided the first, breathtaking splashes of color.

The cool breeze blowing in through the open windows of the car was fragrant with the smell of newly turned earth. Katy reached up with one hand and released the clasp at the nape of her neck. A shake of her head sent her long, raven-black hair tumbling free. She laughed happily as the wind threaded teasing fingers through the thick, luxuriant mass of ebony and swirled it around her shoulders like a black silk cape.

Katy drove the private country road with the easy confidence of long experience. Her father had been the manager of Green Meadows Farm for the past fifteen years, and she knew every twist and turn, every pot hole. The road was the back entrance to the farm. It cut through the surrounding woods, then made a lazy, meandering loop past the scattered cottages of the married workers, before finally ending at the stables behind the Barnetts' big colonial mansion.

The forest thinned, then gave way to an open meadow. To the right, set far off the road, was the small white frame house where Katy had lived since she was a child of six. Braking, she turned in through the open gate. There was a double garage behind the house but Katy stopped the car beside the pickup in the wide drive. There was time enough later to put it away.

As she reached out to turn off the ignition a movement on the porch caught her eye, and she turned her head. Her hand froze in mid-air when she recognized the man standing there in the shadows.

A crawling, tingling sensation ran up over her scalp,

making the hairs on her nape bristle. Damn! If only she'd been more alert, she might have seen him. Then she could have driven on and stayed away until he had gone. The blue pickup had not given her a clue, since it was one of the half dozen or so owned by Green Meadows Farm and identical to the one her father always drove. Katy stared at the tall, broad-shouldered man and silently berated herself for her carelessness. She had known, intuitively, that he would come.

A vague feeling of unease had nagged at her since seeing Trace yesterday at the funeral, but she had pushed it away. Foolishly she had allowed herself to be mesmerized by the signs of spring, lulled into a false sense of security and well-being. It was one of those soft, unseasonably warm days that completely beguiles the senses, and Katy had fallen so totally under its spell that she had forgotten all about Trace Barnett.

As she switched off the engine he moved out of the shadows and stood on the top step, watching her, tall and lean and infinitely dangerous looking. His stance was casual as he waited for her to join him, one arm propped against the porch post, the other on his hip, but Katy was aware that his eyes never left her.

Taking a deep breath, she composed herself, climbed from the car and started up the brick path on legs that were suddenly weak and rubbery. Though well aware that she was being subjected to a thorough, masculine appraisal, when Katy looked directly into those penetrating hazel eyes she almost reeled with shock. They gleamed with a frankly sensual interest which he made no effort to conceal. It was only through sheer strength of will that she was able to clamp down on her emotions and quell the cowardly urge to turn and run. Katy recognized the tingling feeling that raced up her spine for exactly what it was—pure, cold, mindless fear.

There was no specific reason for her fear of Trace. It was strictly a gut level feeling. She had known him nearly all her life, and yet, strangely, did not know him at all. He had been the owner's son, and she merely the daughter of the farm manager, and eleven years his junior. For years their lives had run along a parallel plane, existing at the same time, in the same place, with no point of contact between them. Yet she knew, instinctively, that Trace Barnett spelled danger. She had known that much when she had been only seventeen.

The promise of great beauty had become a reality about that time, and she had blossomed, almost overnight, from a gangly, skinny teenager into a breathtakingly lovely young woman. The transformation had not escaped Trace. During that year before he left the farm she had been aware of the long, speculative looks he directed her way. Cautious and reserved by nature, she had never once acknowledged the open invitation in those wicked hazel eyes. At seventeen she had been far too naive to know the reason for those warm, slumberous glances and that small crooked smile that had set her insides to quivering strangely. But she knew now.

Trace had never approached her openly, but had, nevertheless, managed to let her know that he found her very attractive. Though she had pretended not to notice, she had been both excited and frightened by his attention.

That was four years ago. Now all she felt was stark terror. It had gripped her yesterday at the graveside, when she glanced up and found him staring at her, his face alive with male interest. She had known then that if he stayed, this time he would do more than just look.

Katy forced herself to return his steady gaze as she neared the porch. Trace was the first to break eye contact, and she felt a small sense of victory until she realized that he was now conducting a leisurely inspection of her body, from her tousled black hair to the pink toes peeping out of her strappy sandals. The hot, searing look sent fresh tremors through her. Gritting her teeth, Katy took a deep breath and forced herself to speak.

"Hello, Mr. Barnett." Her soft voice was coated with a thin layer of ice.

Trace's eyes lifted slowly, lingering for just a fraction of a second on the full curves of her breasts, before returning to her face. He smiled. "Hello, Katy."

His voice was low and husky, giving the simple greeting the sensuality of a caress, and Katy stiffened, panic streaking through her. Her heart began to beat like a wild thing against her ribs.

What was it about Trace that disturbed her so? During the past four years she had met, and been unaffected by, a number of interested males. Oh, they had made her nervous and uneasy, but she had never allowed any of them to get close enough to stir the deep well of fear locked inside her. Yet Trace could do it with just a look.

At close quarters he was even more overwhelming than he had seemed yesterday when she had only seen him from a distance. Four years had added maturity to his face and intensified his rugged masculinity. He had the hard, chiseled look one associates with an outdoorsman. His nose was straight and well-modeled, his jaw strong. His lips were well-defined and firm, and when he smiled, they revealed strong, even teeth. Bronze skin was stretched taut and smooth over the prominent bones of his face, and there was a network of fine lines that fanned out from the corners of his eyes. His light brown hair was thick and springy, with a tendency to curl against his nape and over the top of his ears. His hazel eyes were deep-set and hooded, topped by thick, light brown brows and surrounded by short, almost white lashes. Trace was a tall, lean man, with broad shoulders, long legs, and narrow hips. And he was, above all, utterly and devastatingly male.

Katy's throat tightened painfully as she looked at

him. He exuded an earthy sensuality that unnerved her, a raw, primitive virility that reached out and touched her, and made her skin prickle.

He was smiling at her, his eyes amused, as though he knew she found him disturbing. He was right, she did, though not in the way he probably thought. Katy lowered her gaze, afraid her eyes would give her away. Some men, she knew, were turned on as much by fear as by passion.

Reaching into her bag, she pulled out her house key. "I'm afraid my father is not here at the moment. If you'd like to leave a message for him, I'll see that he gets it as soon as he returns." A quiver shook her voice, but there was no mistaking the dismissal in her words.

Katy knew she was probably being very stupid, talking to him that way. Trace was now her father's employer. Yet she couldn't help herself.

Turning away, she inserted the key into the lock. She could see him out of the corner of her eye. Trace was watching her every move with disconcerting interest. She opened the door just a fraction, then hesitated, expecting him to take the hint and leave, but he didn't move. Katy gritted her teeth and looked back over her shoulder, a tight smile on her face. "In any case, I'll be sure and tell him that you came by."

To her surprise, Trace seemed to find her efforts to be rid of him amusing. Mocking laughter glittered in his eyes as he stepped closer and put his hand on the door. "If you don't mind, I'll wait," he said with the arrogant self-confidence of a man accustomed to getting his own way.

She stared at him for a moment, totally dismayed. Her heart began to pound. Oh, God! She didn't want him here! Couldn't he see that? Hazel eyes locked with hers, challenging, daring her to refuse him. Finally she nodded her head in stiff agreement, her mouth thin. "Of course. You're welcome to come in and wait," she lied.

"Thank you," he said dryly.

He motioned for her to precede him, and Katy stepped inside. Every nerve in her body seemed to jump when she heard the door click shut behind them. With jerky steps she walked across the room and placed her bag on an end table. Turning, she found that Trace had stopped just inside the door.

His stance was loose and casual, feet apart, hands stuck in the back pockets of his jeans. His head was thrown back and his eyes were scanning the room intently, noting the homey furniture, the pictures on the wall, the braided rug—every minute detail.

Katy watched him, puzzled by his interest. His gaze flickered back to her face and he smiled. "Do you know, I've never been in your home before?" He sounded surprised, as though it were something he had only just realized.

"Yes, I know," she replied bluntly. Of course he hadn't. Neither had his father nor his stepmother. The Barnetts were very class-conscious people. They didn't consider a mere employee their social equal. When Henry Barnett had wished to speak to her father, he had sent for him to come up to the big house. He would not have dreamed of lowering himself by going to his farm manager's home.

Katy edged toward the door leading into the hall. "If you'll excuse me for a moment, Mr. Barnett, I'll wash up. Then, if you'd like, I'll make some coffee."

Trace folded his long frame into an armchair and smiled. "Fine. Take your time."

In the bathroom Katy quickly washed her hands and ran a comb through her hair, studiously avoiding her pale reflection in the mirror. When she had restored order to her appearance she stood quietly for a moment and pressed her hand against her fluttering stomach. Finally she took a deep breath and retraced her steps, giving Trace a nervous smile as she walked through the living room.

"I'll just be a moment," she said, and quickly pushed through the kitchen door. When it swung shut behind her she closed her eyes and breathed a deep, shuddering sigh.

Barely knowing what she was doing, Katy automatically spooned ground coffee into the coffeepot's basket and filled the reservoir with water. She turned on the switch and watched distractedly as a thin stream of brown liquid slowly filled the glass pot. Her eyes darted toward the living room.

It was strange that in the end Trace had inherited Green Meadows Farm. Henry Barnett had declared repeatedly, and very forcefully, that he would not leave his maverick son one red cent. After quarreling violently with his father four years ago, Trace had walked out, and the old man had never forgiven him. No one knew exactly what the quarrel had been about but, as usual in a city the size of Tyler, the rumors were plentiful. Regardless of the cause, the split had been a serious one, and Trace had not returned to the farm until yesterday.

Katy recalled that when she was a child it had seemed as though Trace was constantly quarreling with his father over one thing or another. A wild one. That was what her father called him, though he said it with the affectionate tolerance of a man who had found a kindred soul.

For Thomas Patrick Donovan had also been a wild one in his time. A big bear of an Irishman, he had roamed the world footloose and fancy-free, working when he chose, drinking when he felt like it, and brawling just for the sheer fun of it. But Tom Donovan's wild days had come to an abrupt end when he met Kathleen O'Shea. Her delicate beauty and gentle ways had ensnared him as nothing else ever could, binding him to her with silken ties of love. He had, quite simply, adored her. After their marriage he had become a model husband and, a year later, a proud father.

Katy's eyes darted once again toward the living room. The same thing could happen to Trace, she supposed, though it didn't seem likely. She doubted that love for a woman would ever tame Trace Barnett. He still had that look of a maverick, a rebel, one who thumbs his nose at the world and goes his own way.

A great many people were surprised and stunned when Henry Barnett's will was read and it was disclosed that Trace had inherited Green Meadows Farm. Katy smiled wryly to herself. Not the least of whom was Saundra Barnett, Henry's young widow. She had fully expected to inherit everything. How shocked she must have been to learn that she would receive only a modest sum in cash.

The coffee maker gurgled to a stop and Katy placed the glass pot on a tray. After adding two cups, cream, and sugar, she picked it up and pushed through the door.

"Here, let me do that." Trace jumped up and took the tray from her hands and placed it on the low coffee table. To Katy's dismay, instead of returning to the chair, he joined her on the sofa. The nervous, panicky feeling intensified, making the hair on the back of her neck stand on end. Clenching her jaw, she picked up the coffeepot and concentrated fiercely on filling the cups.

"Cream and sugar?"

"No, just black."

Katy handed him the cup, being careful not to touch him.

Apparently very much at ease, Trace leaned back against the sofa and drank his coffee slowly. Katy didn't have to look at him to know he was watching her. She could feel his eyes on her. She added sugar to her coffee and watched the swirling, brown liquid intently as she stirred it.

"Tell me, Katy. What have you been doing these past four years, other than growing incredibly beautiful?" he asked softly.

She looked up, and her stomach gave a sickening little lurch. His eyes glittered with a disturbing intensity as they roamed over her, warm and boldly sensual. It was the same look she had surprised on his face yesterday.

Katy stared down at the cup in her hand and ran one finger slowly around the edge. "For the last year I've been working at a nursery school in Tyler. Before that I took care of my mother."

She felt tears stinging the back of her eyes and quickly looked away. It was still difficult to talk about her lovely, brave mother. They had known since Katy was fourteen that Kathleen Donovan was dying of a slow progressive muscular disease, but that had not made her death any easier to take. For six years, during the time when other girls her age were in open rebellion against their parents, Katy had spent every spare moment with her mother, heartbreakingly aware that she was slowly slipping away.

"I'm sorry about your mother, Katy. I know you were very close to her." Trace's voice broke through her sad thoughts, soft and infinitely gentle.

She looked at him then and saw that there was a genuine compassion in his eyes. Somehow she hadn't expected that from him, and it had a devastating effect on her fragile self-control. Her chest was tight with suppressed emotion and her throat hurt, but Katy knew she had to make some reply. Otherwise she was going to burst into tears. Blinking away the moisture in her eyes, she smiled faintly.

"Thank you, Mr. Barnett. Actually, I'm the one who should be offering condolences. My mother died almost a year ago, but you've only just buried your father."

"Ah, but I can't pretend that my father and I were ever close, and there was certainly no love lost between us." Trace smiled dryly. "Therein lies the difference."

Taken aback, Katy looked down at her hands. Her relationship with her parents had always been a warm, loving one. They were a unit, a family. The cold indifference in Trace's voice when he spoke of his father made her shiver. When the silence ran on she searched her mind desperately for something to say.

The problem was solved for her when Trace said, "Tell me, whatever happened to your plans for college? I seem to recall hearing that you wanted to be a teacher."

Sensing criticism, Katy's head jerked up. "There wasn't any money for college. My mother's illness was very costly. Dad had to borrow just to pay for her therapy and medication, and he's still paying off the loan." She stared at him, her blue eyes defiant. "But whatever the cost, whatever the sacrifice, if it added just one day to her life, it was worth it."

He looked at her tenderly and smiled. "Of course it was."

His soft agreement dissolved the small spurt of defensive anger, and Katy felt foolish for having bristled. Being this close to Trace made her nervous and on edge.

He leaned over and placed his cup on the coffee table. The movement strained the soft cotton shirt tautly across his broad back and shoulders. Katy's eyes were drawn irresistibly to the play of flexing muscles beneath the thin material, and she felt her mouth go suddenly dry. She looked away quickly when he sat back and turned sideways on the sofa, draping his arm along the back. Her stomach muscles clenched into a hard knot. She was vitally aware of his hand, resting just inches away from her shoulder.

"It's a pity though," he mused, as his eyes roamed over her face in open admiration. "You would have made a very good teacher. You're the gentle, quiet type that children take to." He paused and grinned. "And I've always found that children have a great appreciation for beautiful things." Reaching out with one finger, he ran it along the delicate curve of her shoulder, and Katy flinched.

"Don't, please," she pleaded desperately. She closed her eyes and shivered, her hands clenched into tight fists in her lap. Her nerves were screaming. She had known he would touch her. He had come here for that purpose, not to see her father. All his soft concern and interest was just a ruse. He was just like all the rest of his kind—rich, influential men who thought they could take whatever they wanted, with no thought for anyone else. However, being her father's employer, Trace was in a much more powerful position than the others she had met.

She stood up. "I think it would be best if you just left a message for my father, Mr. Barnett. I really have no idea when he'll be home."

Trace smiled and stretched his long legs out in front of him. "Oh, he won't be too long. He went into town to pick up a part for the tractor. He should be back any time now."

Not if he stopped off for a drink, Katy thought sadly. That was something he had been doing regularly since her mother's death. Thomas Donovan was a broken man, shattered into a million pieces. The loss of his beloved Kathleen had been a blow from which he had never truly recovered. It didn't happen often, and he never drank during working hours, but when his pain became too much for him to bear, he occasionally sought relief in the bottom of a whiskey bottle. It hurt her to see him grieving so, and she didn't have the heart to scold him.

Katy turned back to the devastatingly attractive man who sat lazily on the sofa, looking at her with a glint of amusement in his eyes. She twisted her hands nervously. "In that case, I'm afraid I really must start dinner, Mr. Barnett."

"That's all right. I'll keep you company in the kitchen. I like to watch a woman being domestic." He grinned and winked. "It's something you don't see very often these days."

Katy wanted to scream! Was the man totally insensitive? She had all but demanded that he leave, and still he would not budge!

During the last three years she had become adept at fending off predatory males. Her beauty had drawn the interest of most of the eligible men in the area at one time or another. At first they found her cool reserve challenging, but when it became evident that she was simply not interested, was in fact repelled by their advances, they quickly moved on to easier game. The male ego is a fragile thing at best, and a woman's complete lack of interest is too wounding to be endured for long.

Trace Barnett, however, was a different breed of animal, and Katy was slowly and alarmingly becoming convinced that he would not be so easily discouraged.

She stared at him wordlessly for a long moment. His dogged determination was unnerving. This man was dangerous and she knew it, yet she could think of no reason for refusing him. "Very well," she replied tightly, and turned on her heel. A muscle twitched in her jaw as she stalked into the kitchen.

Trying her best to ignore him, Katy opened the refrigerator door and pulled out two thick steaks. After scoring the edges, she sprinkled them with seasoning and placed them in a broiler pan, then set it aside. Trace leaned against the counter, his arms crossed over his chest, watching her. Katy was acutely conscious of his long, lean frame, and its aura of pure maleness. Suddenly the kitchen seemed too small. Her nerves were stretched to breaking point, and when he spoke she jumped, her pulse leaping in alarm.

"So you're still hiding from the world," he said softly. It was a statement, not a question, and it caught her completely unaware.

A puzzled frown knit between her brows. Had she missed something? She didn't have the faintest idea what he was talking about. Turning back to the refrigerator, she began to remove the salad ingredients.

"I'm afraid I don't understand."

"I'm talking about your job. It's typical of you to choose one where you seldom come into contact with adults. Men in particular. You were as skittish as a young deer four years ago, but I thought by now you would have outgrown that." He shook his head, his hazel eyes intent on her face. "If anything, you're even more withdrawn."

Katy took two salad bowls from the cabinet and placed them on the counter. She was trying desperately to keep her expression calm, though her insides were quaking. "I took the job in the nursery because I love children. That was why I wanted to become a teacher. Since that field was closed to me, this was the next best thing."

She had not looked at him while she spoke, but kept her eyes on her hands as they broke the lettuce up into small pieces, very slowly and precisely. He had no idea how nervous he was making her, or how terrified she was of breaking down in front of him. Only her father knew and understood, and he wasn't here.

Trace leaned closer and tilted his head to look into her face. He was smiling that crooked little half smile. His eyes were teasing. "If you love kids so much you should have some of your own. You'd make a wonderful mother, Mary Kathleen Donovan. But first you need to become a wife"—he paused, then added with a wicked grin—"and a lover."

His warm breath caressed her ear as the softly whispered, evocative words stroked over her, and she shivered violently. Katy put down the knife she was using to dice tomatoes and clutched the edge of the counter with both hands. She closed her eyes and fought down the hysterical bubble of fear that rose in her throat. She had to get him out of here, somehow, and she had to do it *now*. Lifting a shaking hand, she ran it over her brow.

"Look, Mr. Barnett, I don't think—"

A car door slammed and Tom Donovan's loud, booming voice carried through the open windows. "Katy, darlin', I'm home. Would you be havin' a hot meal ready for a poor starvin' man?"

Katy's eyes flew open in sheer panic. Her father was drunk or close to it. The thick Irish brogue was a dead giveaway. Under normal circumstances it was hardly noticeable, but when he was drinking or his emotions were aroused, he always lapsed into the lilting speech of his youth.

Her stricken gaze swung toward Trace, her blue eyes pleading for understanding. If her father lost this job, he would have a difficult time finding another at his age. He had been middle-aged when he had finally married and settled down. Though he had been a loyal and trustworthy employee, no one wanted to hire a man in his sixties.

The front door banged shut. Katy dried her hands and rushed past Trace.

Her father was standing just inside the living room, and her heart sank when she saw him. His face was flushed and he was definitely unsteady on his feet. Even his thick mane of white hair was untidy. Quickly, she walked over to him and slipped an arm around his waist.

"Dad, where have you been? Mr. Barnett has been waiting for you." It was as much of a warning as she could give him. Katy could only hope that he was sober enough to understand.

Tom Donovan stiffened. "What?"

"Mr. Barnett is in the kitchen, Dad. He was here when I came home."

"I wanted to go over the work schedule with you," Trace said, as he stepped into the room. He hesitated a moment, his attention captured by the expression on Katy's face. The deep-set hazel eyes narrowed, then slid back to the huge man at her side. He stared at him for several seconds, his gaze hard and probing. Then, at last, he seemed to have reached a decision. Shrugging indifferently, he said, "However, since it's so late, we'll leave it until tomorrow."

Katy went limp with relief.

Tom's expression grew anxious. He was not so far gone that he missed the paleness of his daughter's face or the harried look in her eyes. A silent message passed between them, and Katy smiled tremulously, reassured by his presence. Only he knew what an ordeal it had been for her, being here alone with Trace for all this time.

A worried frown creased his brow. "Are you all right, Katy?" he asked softly.

"Yes, Dad."

Trace scowled and walked further into the room. His hard gaze sliced back and forth between Katy and her father.

"Is there some reason why Katy wouldn't be all right?" he demanded with an angry edge to his voice.

"Well . . . er . . . no." Tom looked distinctly uncomfortable. "It's just that Katy has been . . . unwell lately."

"I see," Trace replied thoughtfully, his hazel eyes raking over her.

Katy held her breath, silently praying that he wouldn't probe further. She couldn't bear that.

Finally, after an interminable period of strained silence, he turned and picked up his hat from the chair, then gave the older man a curt nod. "I'll meet you at the stables first thing in the morning, Tom. Good night."

Katy released her hold on her father. Politeness demanded that she see Trace to the door. She was a step behind him when he paused with his hand on the knob and looked down at her, smiling.

"By the way, Katy darlin'," he murmured softly, giving an excellent imitation of her father's Irish brogue. "My name is Trace. Remember that."

Chapter Two

As Katy lifted the tiny blond mite, chubby arms encircled her neck and the child planted a moist, smacking kiss on her cheek.

"Bye, Miss Katy."

Katy smiled and hugged the warm little body to her for a second. "Good-bye, Millie. I'll see you tomorrow."

Still holding the child close, she opened the passenger door of the waiting car and bent over. She smiled at the woman behind the wheel as she sat the little girl on the seat and fastened the safety belt around her. "Millie has had a very big day, Mrs. Carter. At play period she built a sand castle all by herself."

A ferocious frown darkened the little girl's brow. "Yes. An' that rotten Jeff kicked it down," she complained petulantly.

Both women laughed at the expression of pure fury on the cherubic little face.

"Sorry about that." Katy's grin was rueful. "I'm afraid Jeffrey Bond has a bit of a crush on Millie, and like most four-year-old boys, he has a rather strange way of demonstrating his affection."

"Oh, believe me, Miss Donovan, I know how it

goes," Millie's mother replied, still laughing. "Millie is the last of my brood, so I've been through it all before. Love among the pre-school set can sometimes be rather violent."

"Yes, but it all worked out. After he apologized, Jeffrey helped her rebuild her castle, and it was a beauty."

Refusing to be mollified quite so easily, Millie stuck out her bottom lip. "But it wasn't as good as the first one. Jeff don't know how to build a castle." She sniffed disdainfully, turning up her tiny nose and dismissing the little boy's efforts with the haughty superiority of a very young female.

"Well, never mind, angel. Tomorrow you can build another one, and I'll see that Jeff doesn't bother you." Katy smiled at Mrs. Carter and planted another quick kiss on Millie's forehead. "Bye now, sweetheart. I'll see you tomorrow afternoon." Straightening, she closed and locked the passenger door and stepped back. As the car pulled away Millie waved furiously, and Katy laughed and waved back.

She watched until they were out of sight, then turned back to the nursery school entrance. A satisfied smile eased the tiredness from her face.

Katy entered the small office and locked the door behind her. After closing the draperies, she turned and stepped through the door to the right of the desk and walked down the long hall, stopping several times along the way to pick up the stray toys that littered the floor. By the time she reached the end of the hall her arms were full. The door to the playroom was slightly ajar. Giving it a nudge with her hip, she pushed it open and walked inside, then stopped short at the sight that greeted her.

Her friend and employer, Jane Cawley, was down on her hands and knees, her jean-covered behind stuck up in the air as she wriggled the upper half of her body under one of the large, extremely low tables.

"What on earth are you doing?" Katy laughed openly at her friend's undignified position.

"I'm . . . trying . . . to clean up this . . . gooey . . . mess," Jane gasped, groping still farther under the table. "There . . . I've got it!" Grunting with every move, she began to wriggle backward, and Katy laughed harder as Jane crawfished from under the table. When she extricated her head, Jane turned and flopped down on the floor. Her face was beet red. The short, brown hair that normally hugged her face, pixie fashion, was sticking up at all angles. Still panting from her exertions, Jane lowered her gaze to the squashed peanut-butter-and-jelly sandwich in her hand and made a face of utter revulsion. "Yuck! Would you look at this revolting mess."

Jane pushed herself up from the floor and walked over to the sink in the corner, depositing the mangled sandwich in the trash before washing the sticky remains from her fingers. "How I stand the little monsters for eight hours every day, I don't know. I need to have my head examined."

"Oh, come on now. Who are you kidding?" Katy gave her friend a reproving look. "You love every minute of it, and you know it."

"I know, I know," Jane conceded with a rueful grin, as she turned to help Katy with the chairs. "I just have to complain now and then or people really will think I'm crazy. But you're right. I do love taking care of children. I thought I'd go bonkers when my own became teenaged and got involved in so many outside activities that I hardly ever saw them. I was suffering from what is commonly known as the empty nest syndrome. The smartest thing I ever did was to open this nursery school." She smiled at Katy and winked. "And the second smartest thing I ever did was to hire you."

Katy returned her friend's smile but made no comment. Funny how things work out, she mused. She had taken this job out of desperation, and it had turned out to be one of the best things that had ever happened to her. It didn't pay much, but she enjoyed the work, and she absolutely adored each and every one of the pint-sized tyrants. An added bonus was the close friendship that had developed between herself and Jane during the year she had worked at the nursery. Due to her reserved nature and the demands that had been made on her time during her teenage years, Katy had not developed any close friendships, and therefore valued this one all the more.

Jane was a small, vivacious woman in her late thirties. An eternal optimist, she bounced through life thoroughly enjoying each day, intensely interested in everything and everyone. Though she was not particularly pretty, no one ever noticed. She had laughing eyes and an incandescent smile that made you feel good just to be around her. She was a bubbly, outgoing extrovert, the direct opposite of Katy.

When the chairs were stacked, Jane turned toward the kitchen. "Come on. Let's have a cup of coffee and prop our feet up for a few minutes before we leave."

In the kitchen Jane poured out two mugs of coffee and handed one to Katy. Kicking off her shoes, she curled herself into the corner of the battered old couch that occupied one wall and tucked her feet under her. She looked at Katy and patted the adjacent cushion. "Come sit down. I'm dying to know what's going on at the farm. I heard only this morning that Trace has inherited Green Meadows. Is that true?"

Katy almost laughed aloud at the avid curiosity written on Jane's face. She knew she really shouldn't be surprised that news of Henry Barnett's will had already spread. It was next to impossible to keep anything a secret in Tyler. The city had grown to a respectable size, but in many ways had retained its small town attitude. As the richest, most powerful family in that part of Texas, the Barnetts had always been the subject of a great deal of speculation and gossip. The fact that Trace had inherited the farm was bound to start tongues wagging.

Katy sat down on the couch. "Yes. It's true."

"Ooohhh, isn't that delicious!" Jane squealed with delight. "I'll bet that witch, Saundra, is ready to have a stroke. The only reason she married Henry Barnett was to get her greedy little hands on his money. And now she's been left high and dry."

"Not quite. Though she'll have no share in the farm or any of the other family holdings, I believe she inherited a modest amount in cash." Katy took a sip of coffee, then smiled wryly. "Of course, what the Barnetts call a modest amount would probably be a fortune to other people."

"Mmmmm. Is she going to stay on at the farm, do you think?"

"Your guess is as good as mine. I make it a point to stay as far away from the Barnetts as I possibly can."

"Humph! I can't say that I blame you. Henry was a first-class snob, and so is that high-and-mighty alley cat he married," Jane burst out indignantly.

Jane and Saundra Barnett were the same age and had attended school together, but that was the only thing they had in common. Saundra was a brittle, sophisticated woman. She had thoroughly enjoyed the affluence and social position her marriage provided, while making no pretense of caring for her elderly husband. Her frequent, passionate affairs were common knowledge.

In one of her lightning-quick changes of mood, Jane's anger disappeared, and her face lit up with a smile, her eyes twinkling with mischief. "Tell me, is Trace still the gorgeous hunk he was four years ago?"

Katy's eyes grew round in feigned shock. "Why, Jane Cawley! And you a married woman! Whatever would Frank say?" She gave her a stern look and shook her head. "Gorgeous hunk, indeed!"

"I may be married but I'm not blind. And Frank

wouldn't care. He knows he's the love of my life," her friend answered pertly. "So come on, tell me about Trace. Is he still as sinfully attractive as he was?"

Katy looked down at the mug of coffee she held in her hand and slowly traced one finger around the rim. She didn't want to talk about Trace. She didn't even want to think about him. It tied her insides up in knots. "Yes, I suppose you could say that he's attractive . . . if you like the type."

Jane looked amused. "And just what type is he?"

"Dangerous."

The word slipped out before she thought, and Katy was instantly appalled that she had voiced her feelings aloud.

The blank astonishment on Jane's face slowly faded as she stared at Katy's bent head. She pursed her lips together thoughtfully. "Now that's a very revealing reaction. Don't tell me. Let me guess. Trace made a pass, didn't he?"

Katy looked up and smiled weakly, her cheeks pink. "No. It's not that."

"Then what is it? You don't usually react so violently toward a man. You just look right through most of them, as though they didn't exist."

"Oh, I don't know." Agitated, Katy waved her hand in the air in a vague, frustrated gesture. "It's just that he's so—so . . ."

"Sexy?" Jane's eyes were dancing as she asked the provocative question.

"Yes. I guess so." The agreement was given begrudgingly. Katy stood up and walked to the sink and rinsed out her cup. Just thinking about Trace made her feel quivery. Turning, she leaned back against the counter and gripped the edge with both hands. Her troubled expression revealed her inner confusion. "I don't know. Maybe it's just my overactive imagination, but he makes me so nervous and jittery. The way he looks at me . . . the things he says. It gives me this crawly sensation. I get the overpowering feeling he's up to something."

"Oh-ho! And I can just imagine what! Listen, honey. I wouldn't doubt my instincts if I were you. Trace has always had an eye for good-looking women, and I somehow can't see him passing up a gorgeous thing like you, especially since you live practically on his doorstep."

Katy pushed away from the counter and stooped to pick up her purse from beside the couch. "I'm afraid this is one woman he'll just have to pass up. I want no part of him . . . or any man."

"Oh, Katy, don't say that," Jane replied sadly. "Marriage with the right person can be wonderful. And, besides, you were born to be a mother. Why, you love every one of the little imps who comes here."

The words sent a wave of longing through Katy, so strong it was almost a physical pain, but she gritted her teeth and fought it down. "That's right. I do. And for me, they'll just have to be enough." She had abandoned all hope of having a family of her own three years ago. For her it was impossible. She knew Jane was puzzled by her attitude, but it couldn't be helped. She couldn't explain, not even to her.

"Katy Donovan! I swear, sometimes you make me so mad I could—"

"My, my. Don't tell me you two are having an argument?"

The two women jumped, then laughed as they turned to see Frank Cawley standing propped against the door frame. A pleasant man with average features, he was the calm, pipe-smoking type, and the perfect counterbalance for Jane's bouncy, effervescent personality. Outside of her parents, they were the most ideally suited couple Katy had ever known.

Jane catapulted herself off the couch straight into her husband's arms, giving him a hard kiss on the mouth, which he returned with enthusiasm. "Hi, darling." She sighed happily, leaning back within his embrace.

"Hello, crazy lady." Frank gave her an affectionate squeeze and ruffled her short-cropped hair, then turned his direct gaze on Katy. "Now, tell me, beautiful. Why was this wife of mine lighting into you like a shrew?"

"Oh, it's the same old thing," Jane spat out disgustedly, before Katy could answer. "She absolutely refuses to have anything to do with men, especially Trace Barnett." Spinning around, she planted her hands on her hips and glared. "You know, Katy, you could do a lot worse."

"Honestly, Jane! Even if he *is* interested, which I seriously doubt, you don't really think marriage is what he has in mind, do you? People like the Barnetts don't marry farm workers' daughters."

"Mary Kathleen Donovan! Don't you dare let me hear you say such a stupid thing again! You're just as good as anyone. And a lot better than most. Certainly better than that bitch, Saundra, and she married a Barnett, even if it was that old snob, Henry."

Katy laughed nervously. Her friend's vehemence startled her. "Jane, for heaven's sake! Don't get so upset over nothing. I merely said the man makes me nervous, and now you're screaming at me because I won't marry him." She turned bewildered blue eyes on Frank. "Does she always jump to conclusions like this?"

He grinned. "Always. Especially when she's defending someone she loves. A regular little tigress, that's my Jane."

"Yes, well. Sorry, love. I didn't mean to get so carried away." Jane smiled ruefully. "It's just that you're one of my very favorite people, and I'll not let anyone run you down. Not even you."

"And I have to say, Katy, I think you're wrong about Trace," Frank added softly, as he took his pipe and tobacco pouch from his pocket. He dipped the bowl into the pouch and filled it, carefully tamping down the loose tobacco with his thumb. "When a young woman is as warm and sweet and lovely as you, all other considerations fade in importance."

Katy gave him a bitter smile. She liked Frank. He was a good friend, and one of the few men with whom she felt at ease. But he was still a man. "Well, this is all rather academic, isn't it? I've only talked with the man once since he returned."

On the way home Katy thought about Jane's indignant outburst. She hadn't meant to give the impression that she thought herself inferior to the Barnetts. She didn't. At least not in the ways that mattered. But neither did she fool herself into thinking they were on an equal footing. The Barnetts, and their kind, had a very definite advantage over ordinary people, an advantage they did not hesitate to use—power and influence. Katy had learned, the hard way, that without it you were helpless and vulnerable. She also knew that theirs was a closed society. They socialized only with people within their own circle, and they married only their own kind. And if one of their group was threatened, the other members of the pack closed ranks around them. You didn't stand a chance if you crossed swords with people like the Barnetts.

Katy drove home automatically, her mind occupied with her gloomy reflections. It was not until she turned into the drive that she realized her thoughts had once again strayed to Trace. Stop it! she told herself harshly. Stop thinking about him! The man was becoming an obsession. And why, she didn't know. It had been four days since that evening she had arrived home to find him waiting on the porch.

On the surface, nothing he had done or said that night could be faulted. Not really. Was it all just her imagination? Katy laughed in sudden self-derision. Maybe she was just becoming vain. Had she become so accustomed to fending off men that she automatically assumed every one she met was going to make a pass? Lord, surely she hadn't become as self-absorbed as all that!

No, Katy assured herself firmly as she climbed from the car. That look in his eyes, and the silky, sensuous tone of his voice when he spoke to her hadn't been a product of her imagination. But now that she'd had time to think about it, she realized his flirtatious manner probably didn't mean a thing. She had forgotten, for a while, that Trace and his crowd played by a different set of rules. It was probably second nature to him to flirt with every passably attractive woman he met. It was instinctive, an automatic reflex. It meant no more to him than blinking. Once he had walked out the door, he had probably forgotten all about her. Fool that she was, she'd spent the last four days worrying and fretting over how she was going to discourage him without jeopardizing her father's job, when if she'd just given it a little serious thought, she would have realized that the whole thing was ludicrous.

Katy unlocked the front door and stepped inside, then leaned back against the panel and closed her eyes. So why wouldn't this crawly feeling go away? a tiny voice whispered.

When her father's truck pulled into the drive Katy was standing at the sink, peeling potatoes. The sleeves of her blue and red plaid shirt were rolled up to her elbows, revealing the delicate bones of her wrists and forearms. Faded jeans hugged her hips and thighs like a soft second skin. Her raven-black hair was sleeked away from her face and held at her nape by a tortoise-shell clasp.

The front screen door banged against its frame. Katy didn't even look up. "Hi, Dad. I'm out here in the kitchen," she called over her shoulder.

"Whatever you're cooking smells delicious." Tom poked his head inside the kitchen door and smiled coaxingly. "I hope it will stretch to three. I invited Trace home to share our dinner."

It took a moment for his words to soak in. When they did, Katy turned slowly, her eyes wide with shock. She stared at her father, unable to believe what she'd heard. Then her gaze slid past him and collided with a pair of glinting hazel-green eyes, and the color slowly drained from her face.

A mocking, half smile played around one corner of Trace's mouth. His amused expression told her he was well aware of her dilemma.

"I hope this isn't an inconvenience, Katy. If it is, please feel free to say so." His tone was very polite, very proper, but Katy knew he was taunting her. Trace was quite obviously enjoying her discomfort.

"Nonsense, nonsense," her father cut in. Sniffing appreciatively, he stepped over to the stove and inspected the bubbling pots. "Katy is frying chicken, and she always cooks twice what we need. Now, come on. It's all settled." He motioned for Trace to follow as he started toward the door. "I'll show you where you can wash up, then I'll fix us a drink before dinner."

Katy stared at the two broad, retreating backs. How could he do this? How *could* he? Her father knew how she felt! But more important, he knew perfectly well that a man in his position simply did not invite someone like Trace home for dinner. Why, old Henry would have had apoplexy had he even suggested such a thing!

The small table set beneath the back window drew her eyes, and she groaned. She didn't suppose Trace had ever eaten in a kitchen in his life. Flooded with a feeling of helplessness and frustrated anger, Katy jerked open a cabinet and snatched a plate from the stack. She rummaged through the cutlery drawer for the proper utensils, then marched across the room and banged the items down on the table. Well, if he intends to eat here, he'll have to, she thought angrily. They didn't even have a dining room!

When Trace reappeared, Katy was standing at the stove, gently turning each piece of chicken, exposing the golden brown crust that had already formed on one side. She kept her eyes on the bubbling oil.

"I'm sorry, Mr. Barnett, if my father's invitation put you in an awkward position or embarrassed you in any way," she stated stiffly.

There was a short pause before Trace replied. "I'm neither embarrassed nor did I feel any particular obligation to accept your father's invitation. I never do anything I don't want to do." He stared at her coolly, his head cocked to one side. "I would never have thought you were an inverted snob, Katy Donovan."

The needling taunt stiffened her spine. She held her head high and turned to face him. "You must surely know that your father would not even have considered coming to this house for dinner. And if my father had been foolish enough to extend an invitation, I have no doubt he would have been put in his place, very quickly and very firmly." Katy's soft voice was trembling with icy indignation. How dare he call her a snob!

The hazel eyes narrowed ominously. "One thing you'd better learn, Katy, and learn quickly. I am *not* my father." The low fury in his voice sent a shiver through her. "We saw eye to eye on practically nothing. So whatever preconceived notions you've formed about me, you can just throw out the window. I won't be tarred with the same brush, Katy. I'm my own man."

Confused by the harshness of his words and his determination to make her believe them, Katy mumbled a quick, "I'm sorry," and turned back to the stove. As she opened the oven door and slid in the tray of biscuits she felt his eyes boring a hole in her back. Finally, without a word, he turned and walked back into the living room.

A few minutes later her father bustled into the kitchen to prepare the drinks he had promised. Katy turned on him. Her eyes were brimming with tears.

"How could you do this, Dad? You knew I didn't want that man here. How could you?"

The anguish in her voice brought his movements to a halt. He put down the two glasses he had taken from the cupboard and turned to her. Big, paw-like hands cupped around her face to tilt it up for his inspection. Smiling down into her troubled eyes, he saw the fear and anxiety there and shook his head sadly.

"Oh, Katy, Katy." He sighed heavily. "Darlin', Trace won't hurt you. He's a good man. Can't you see that? Why, over the past week he has earned the respect and admiration of every man on the place." Tom's weathered brow creased with worry as he searched her face. Lowering his voice, he spoke to her soothingly, tenderly. "Believe me, sweetheart, if I didn't know I could trust him, I wouldn't let him near you."

Katy swallowed hard and lowered her eyes. Her chin quivering, she stared at a button on the front of his shirt. "All right, Dad. I won't say any more. It's too late now to do anything about it anyway."

The meal, and the rest of the evening, passed very smoothly, despite Katy's jittery nerves. Trace and her father consumed their food with the hearty appreciation of men who have spent the day out of doors doing physical labor. Katy barely touched hers. The talk centered around the farm—which mares were due to foal, which pastures were in need of attention, the cost of grain. It was strictly man talk and she was happy to sit back and let it all wash over her.

After the meal Katy served the men their coffee in the living room, then returned to the kitchen to do the washing up, grateful for the excuse to escape. She washed each dish carefully and slowly to draw out the chore as long as possible. As her hands went about the familiar task she stared past her reflection in the window at the dark shadows of the woods behind the house.

A storm was building up in the distance. Above the bare branches the sky glowed intermittently with eerie flashes of white as lightning streaked downward from a livid line of black clouds. Katy eyed it hopefully. If it moved this way, perhaps Trace would leave.

She sighed as she placed the last dish in the drain rack and pulled the stopper from the sink. What was the reason for his sudden friendly attitude? She thought about his taut anger when she had apologized for her father's presumptuousness in inviting him here. Was that it? Was he trying to demonstrate that he was not a carbon-copy of his father, that he had no intention of following his lead? If so, was he doing it out of sheer obstinacy, a determination to go against his father's wishes? Or did he really want to develop a better working relationship with his employees?

Henry Barnett's haughty lord of the manor attitude had always irritated Katy. Her father liked it no better than she, but he managed to shrug it off. He knew his worth, and he loved this farm and his work too much to be bothered by his employer's social prejudices. Thomas Donovan had a way with animals, particularly horses. He had worked with them all his life, both in Ireland and the states, and his knowledge and experience were unsurpassed. Henry Barnett had not liked him, had thought him too proud by far for a mere working man, but he had been no one's fool. He had known exactly what kind of manager he had in Tom Donovan.

Katy supposed she should be grateful that Trace treated her father with the respect and deference his age and experience deserved. Drying her hands, she hung the towel on the rack in the pantry. The low rumble of male voices drew her gaze toward the living room, and her lips compressed into a bitter line. At least with Henry they hadn't had to worry about him dropping in any time it suited him.

There was hardly a pause in the conversation when

Katy entered the room and slipped quietly into a chair. She doubted that either man had even noticed her presence, which, for some perverse reason, annoyed her intensely.

While they continued their discussion about the work schedule and the various changes Trace wanted to make around the farm, Katy took a half-finished needlepoint pillow cover from her sewing basket and concentrated fiercely on the in and out movements of the needle she was stabbing through the canvas. She was making an absolute mess of it. Tomorrow she would have to pick out every single stitch. Tonight, however, she needed something to divert her attention, anything that would keep her gaze from straying to the large, lean man across the room.

He gestured with his hand suddenly and Katy glanced up, her eyes drawn by the movement. She studied him thoughtfully through the long sweep of her lashes. He sat deep in the chair, his long legs stretched out lazily in front of him, one arm hooked casually over the back. His sleeves were rolled up, revealing tanned, muscular forearms, covered with a generous sprinkling of short, light hair, bleached almost white by constant exposure to the sun. Irresistibly, her gaze traveled over his long, powerful body, noting the way his jeans were molded over his narrow hipbones, the curling chest hair visible at the V-shaped opening of his shirt, the breadth of his shoulders. It seemed to her there was a careless sensuality in his every move. When her gaze lifted to his firm, masculine lips an icy shiver feathered up her spine, and she tore her eyes away.

Katy frowned down at the hopelessly knotted canvas in her lap. What was there about Trace? All evening long her gaze had been drawn to him, like steel to a magnet. It was unnerving. Why was she so intensely aware of him? Most men she simply ignored, their presence never penetrating the icy shield she had formed around herself. But somehow Trace had. And she didn't like it. Since that moment in the cemetery, almost a week ago, when she had looked up and met those glittering hazel eyes, her defenses had begun to crack.

It was a little after ten when the rumble of thunder began to make itself heard. The sound drew Trace's attention and he rose, reluctantly.

"I guess I'd better be going. If I don't leave now, I'll be caught in the deluge." At the door he turned back and gave Katy a slow smile. "Thank you again, Katy, for a delicious meal. I enjoyed it." His gaze shifted to her father. "Tom, I'll see you at the stables in the morning."

Katy and her father barely had time to say a quick good night and he was gone. The suddenness of his departure and his casual, almost distant attitude toward her all evening left her slightly bemused, a feeling that was rapidly replaced by relief.

Two hours later Katy lay staring at the ceiling above her bed, listening to the rain drumming on the roof. She couldn't sleep, and she knew why. Every time she started to drift off, she was haunted by a pair of taunting hazel-green eyes, laughing at her. As much as she hated to admit it, Katy knew Trace was responsible for this indefinable, restless longing. For three years her normal sexual urges had been suppressed, anesthetized by shock. In that time she had felt nothing for any man—no pull of the senses, no heady awareness, not even dislike. She had been completely numb. But now, slowly and surely, Trace was pulling her out of that undemanding, unfeeling state, simply by the force of his presence. His raw masculinity was too potent to be ignored. It was awakening in her responses she did not want to feel, making her acutely aware of her own femininity. It didn't help to tell herself she didn't want a relationship with any man. Her healthy, young body simply would not listen.

She raised herself up on one elbow and punched her feather pillow into a soft cloud, but it didn't help ease the tension. Stifling a moan, she rolled onto her side and stared into the darkness. The small mantel clock in the living room had chimed two o'clock before her eyelids finally fluttered shut.

Chapter Three

Moving the vacuum cleaner back and forth in long, sweeping strokes, Katy slowly made her way across the braided oval rug. A red paisley bandanna was tied around her glistening black hair to protect it from the dust. A red halter top and cut-off jeans made up the rest of her housecleaning attire.

When she reached the end of the rug, she bent down and flicked off the switch, and the vacuum cleaner whined to a stop. Sighing in relief at the cessation of the noise, she walked to the wall socket and pulled the plug. When the machine had been returned to its place in the hall storage closet, Katy padded barefoot into the kitchen.

Taking a glass from the cabinet, she filled it with cool water from the tap and drank it down thirstily. As she placed the empty glass on the counter her gaze automatically wandered out of the window above the sink to the rolling, tree-covered acreage beyond the backyard. In just three weeks the view had changed completely. Every branch was now draped with the lush, intensely green foliage of early spring. Wild flowers of every color and description edged the forest and spilled over into the open meadow. Berry vines twined their way over the fences and through the undergrowth.

Katy sighed and turned away from the beauty of the warm spring day. Tomorrow she would go roaming, but today she had chores to finish.

The dryer buzzed as she stepped out onto the small, screened-in porch which doubled as utility and laundry room. At almost the same moment, the washing machine ended its spin cycle and whirred to a stop. Pulling the warm clothes from the dryer, Katy dumped them into an empty wicker basket, then transferred the damp laundry from the washer to the dryer. When it was again humming, she hefted the basket to the small utility table and began methodically to fold the clean clothes.

A pickup rumbled to a stop in the drive, and a second later a truck door was slammed. The sounds sent Katy's glance through the open doorway to the kitchen wall clock. It was only a few minutes past four. A look of pleased surprise brightened her face. For once her father was home early. Actually he wasn't required to work on Saturdays and Sundays, but try telling him that. Hearing his heavy footsteps cross the tiled kitchen floor, she pushed a loose strand of hair away from her face and glanced over her shoulder.

"Hi, Dad. You're home early, aren't you?"

Tom stopped in the doorway. "Yes. I . . . ah . . . forgot to mention this morning that we've been invited up to the big house for dinner tonight. I thought I'd better warn you so you'd have time to get ready." He eyed his daughter apprehensively, waiting for the reaction he knew would come. He wasn't disappointed.

Katy turned slowly, her blue eyes huge. "You've *got* to be kidding!" The words were dragged from her throat in a hoarse whisper.

"No, I assure you I'm not. Trace invited us a couple of days ago." A faint flush darkened Tom's cheeks. "I guess I just forgot to mention it."

Her heart began to beat frantically. The startling

pronouncement had caught her completely off guard. During the past two weeks, since the night he had shared their dinner, Trace had not come near her. She had seen him from a distance several times, usually in the company of her father, and he had waved and called a greeting, but that was all. With each passing day it had become more and more obvious he was not going to seek her out, and she had begun to relax, her life resuming its normal, placid routine as her worries concerning Trace receded. She had even chided herself for having been a complete and utter fool. Now this.

"Well, I'm sorry. I can't go. You'll just have to make my excuses for me," she blurted out in a panic-stricken rush.

"No, Katy. I will not."

The words hit her like a slap in the face, and her head jerked back in shock.

"You're going to get yourself dressed up and you're going with me up to the big house. You will eat dinner and make pleasant conversation and behave like the well-mannered young lady your mother taught you to be," Tom continued relentlessly. His voice was sure and firm, and there was a look on his face she had never seen before.

The washing machine was behind her and Katy stepped back, clutching at it for support. She shook her head. "But I can't, Dad. You know I can't!"

"You can and you will," he stated emphatically. "Now listen to me, Katy. There will be no excuses and there will be no more running away. I've been too lenient with you. I can see that now. Ever since that incident three years ago I've shielded and humored you and allowed you to hide from the world. I kept thinking that you would eventually get over it, that the horror of it would fade and you would resume a normal life." Tom's wide shoulders drooped, and suddenly he looked very tired, very old. "I was wrong. You haven't recovered because you haven't allowed yourself to forget. You've kept it locked inside you, and it's ruining your life." He gestured furiously with his hand. "Well, no more! Katy, you simply cannot allow one tragic incident to color your whole outlook on life. I won't allow it!"

Stunned speechless, Katy stared at him, all the color slowly draining from her face. The harsh tone of his voice had shocked her even more than his words. All her life her father had treated her with a gentleness that bordered on reverence. She could count on the fingers of one hand the times he had raised his voice to her in anger, thereby making it a most effective weapon. And there was no doubt that he was angry now.

A turmoil of conflicting emotions twisted her insides into a hard knot. She didn't want to go to Trace's home for dinner. Some deep-seated, primitive instinct warned her that to do so would be asking for trouble. Yet she depended on her father's continued support. It was absolutely essential to her peace of mind. The love and caring she'd received from her parents had been the glue which had held her shattered life together. Without it she would fly apart. There was really no choice. Swallowing her fear, Katy closed her eyes and nodded.

"Very well, Dad. I'll go," she said softly, her voice trembling.

Four hours later, pale and quivering with nerves, Katy sat beside her father as he brought their pickup to a stop in the U-shaped drive in front of the Barnetts' colonial mansion. She was strung taut, fighting down the nausea that churned in her stomach. Katy stared at the stately pillars marching across the front veranda with wide, fearful eyes. In the fifteen years during which she had lived at Green Meadows, she had never once been inside the big house. She doubted that her father had seen more of it than the study before Trace had taken over. Now, here they were, the two of them, about to have dinner with the new owner and possibly his young stepmother.

Her breath caught in her throat. Oh, God! She had forgotten all about Saundra. The woman had always treated Katy and her mother as though they were beneath her contempt. Katy could just imagine what she thought of this sudden turn of events.

"Do you think Saundra will be here?" she asked as her father opened his door and climbed from the truck.

He held the door open and looked at her across the width of the seat. "I've no idea, Katy girl. But even if she is, I want you to remember that you are a Donovan, and that is something to be proud of."

Katy smiled. Tom Donovan bowed and scraped to no man . . . or woman. Like all Irishmen, he was filled with a fierce, uncrushable pride, a trait Henry Barnett had found almost intolerable.

Katy was not without the Donovan pride herself. When her father assisted her from the cab of the pickup her eyes sparkled with determination. She was going to remain cool and calm, and get through this evening with her dignity intact if it killed her. After adjusting the full sleeves and scooped neck of her blue silk blouse and smoothing the imaginary wrinkles from the long blue and aqua patterned skirt, she slipped her hand through her father's arm and tilted her chin. "Shall we go?"

He beamed down at her, his eyes glowing with pride. "That's my Katy," he whispered softly.

Katy held her head high as they walked up the pebbled path. For nothing in the world would she let these people see that, inside, she was a quaking mass of nerves.

The sound of raised voices reached them when they stepped onto the veranda. Saundra's shrill tones carried clearly through the open window.

"I tell you, Trace, it simply is *not* done. Your father would not approve of this at all."

"When are you going to get it through your head that whether or not my father would have approved means less than nothing to me? This farm and this house belong to me now, and things will be done my way."

Katy cast her father a nervous glance, and he reached out a hand and rang the bell. The voices ceased. Within a few seconds, Mattie, the Barnetts' housekeeper, appeared at the door.

"Good evening, Mattie." Tom greeted the woman with a friendly smile. "I believe we're expected."

"Yes, of course." Mattie cast a worried glance over her shoulder as they stepped into the entrance hall. She took Katy's lacy white shawl and draped it over her arm. "If you'll just wait right here, I'll tell Mr. Trace you've arrived."

"That won't be necessary, Mattie."

Startled by the terse command, Katy's head swung around, her eyes opening wide at the sight of Trace, framed in the arched doorway to their left. Except at his father's funeral, she had never before seen him dressed so formally. The dark blue suit fit his long, lean frame to perfection. Against the crisp white of his shirt his tanned skin looked like polished bronze. Jane was right, Katy thought distractedly. The only word to describe him was devastating.

For just a second grim, harsh anger was visible in the lines of his face, but it faded quickly when his eyes lit on Katy.

She had taken extra pains with her appearance. Her makeup had been applied with care, and she had swept her hair into a shining knot on the top of her head. Soft tendrils were allowed to escape in front of her ears and across the nape of her neck for a softening effect.

The frank admiration in Trace's expression as his eyes ran over the more sophisticated hairdo brought a blush to her cheeks. It deepened as his inspection continued. His intent gaze traveled slowly from the top of her head to the strappy white sandals on her feet. There was a dark, smoldering look in his deep-set eyes as they returned to her face that in no way matched the coolness of his voice.

"I'm glad you could make it," he said politely, and gestured to the room behind him. "Won't you come in?"

Katy's pulse was fluttering nervously as she stepped toward the door. When Trace's large hand settled against the small of her back, her heart began to pound as though it were trying to get out of her body. She quickened her step to try to elude his touch, but the hand remained firmly in place.

The room they entered was large and well-proportioned, furnished with a harmonious collection of different period pieces. The overall effect was elegant, but definitely inviting. Katy was immediately conscious of the atmosphere of wealth and good taste all around her, but before her eyes could take in any specific details, Trace was directing her attention to the blonde woman ensconced on the sofa.

"Of course you know my stepmother, Saundra."

Katy shot him a quick glance. Had his voice held just a hint of sardonic amusement? She couldn't tell from his impassive face.

"Hello, Mrs. Barnett," she said politely, refocusing her attention on the woman.

Saundra Barnett flicked her a cool, disinterested glance and nodded curtly. "Miss Donovan." Her mouth curled slightly as her pale blue eyes slid over Katy's simple skirt and blouse. She looked pointedly down at her own elegant red chiffon dress and sent Katy a scornful smile.

Beside her, Katy felt Trace stiffen.

"Stop it, Saundra." The command was issued in a

snarl, the low, steely voice holding a definite warning, and his stepmother widened her eyes in feigned innocence.

"Why, darling, I didn't say a word."

As Katy feared, the small, malicious act set the tone for the entire evening. Saundra was never overtly rude. She didn't dare risk another reprimand from Trace. She contented herself with snide little innuendos and cutting double-edged remarks. Her words were not blatantly insulting. They were designed to belittle, to embarrass, to make Katy and her father feel out of place and uncomfortable. If she had been gracious and polite, she might have accomplished her purpose. Katy's shyness and extreme nervousness might have worked against her to make her appear awkward and fumbling. But Saundra had misjudged her opponent, and in doing so, had made a bad tactical error. There was nothing guaranteed to stiffen Katy's spine more than ridicule. Her father's fierce pride, combined with her mother's quiet dignity, was a formidable weapon against Saundra's petty viciousness. Katy met every thrust with a cool composure that seemed to infuriate the older woman.

During the meal Saundra switched her attention from Katy to Trace, talking to him in a warm, sensuous tone, and touching him whenever possible, sliding her pale blue eyes over him like a hungry cat that has just spotted its next meal.

At first Katy was surprised. Then she recalled the rumors that had circulated when Trace left the farm four years ago. One of them was that Trace had been far too friendly with his young stepmother, that he had, in fact, been in love with her. It was said that when the situation had come to his father's attention they had quarreled, and Henry had ordered him to leave. Katy had not believed it at the time, but now she wondered. Saundra's attitude was definitely possessive.

After dinner, coffee was served in the living room

and Katy began to glance at her watch, wondering how long it would be before they could leave without seeming impolite. They had just settled down with their coffee when Mattie appeared in the doorway.

"I'm sorry to interrupt you, Mr. Trace," she said hesitantly. "But Nate Pearson is here. He wants to talk with Mr. Donovan. He says it's urgent."

Before she had finished speaking, Tom was on his feet and heading toward the door. "That will be about Starbright," he explained quickly to Trace. "She's ready to foal at any moment. She's been behaving strangely, and I told Nate to stay with her and call me if anything developed."

"I see," Trace replied, following Tom into the hall.

Nate Pearson was waiting just inside the door. The three men huddled together in serious conversation for a moment, the low murmur of their voices drifting into the room, their words indistinguishable. Then suddenly Tom jerked open the front door and strode out, with Nate on his heels. Trace closed it behind them and returned to the living room.

"I'm sorry, Katy, but there's an emergency down at the stables, and your father felt he should be there. Since it's likely he'll be busy for several hours, possibly even all night, I told him I'd see you home."

Katy stood up, alarmed. "Thank you, but please don't trouble yourself on my account. I'm quite capable of getting home by myself."

"Nevertheless, I'll drive you."

"Oh, no! Really, that's not necessary," she protested quickly. The last thing Katy wanted was to be cooped up in a car with Trace. "I can walk. It's not that far."

"I wouldn't hear of it."

"Oh, for God's sake, Trace!" Saundra spat out irritably. "Let the girl walk! It won't hurt her. After all, she's only . . ."

"That's enough, Saundra!" Trace snapped. He glared at her, his hazel eyes narrowed into glittering slits of green ice. "Miss Donovan is my guest, and I'm going to see her home. I'm not going to tell you again that from now on things are going to be done my way. If you don't like that, then I suggest you pack your bags and leave."

Saundra blanched. "Trace! You don't mean that!"

"I mean it." The flat statement left no room for doubt. Turning his back on the shocked woman, he looked at Katy. "I'll get your wrap."

Five seconds after he had left the room, Saundra turned on her like a spitting cat. Her face was contorted into a livid mask of rage. "Stay away from him, do you hear me! He's mine! I should have married Trace in the first place, not his father. And now I'm going to. And I'm not going to let a stupid little farm girl stand in my way. So if you know what's good for you, you'll remember your place." Her pale eyes raked over Katy contemptuously. "You're just the daughter of a hired hand, and don't you forget it."

Katy looked back at her in sick disgust. Would Trace really marry his father's widow? Saundra was only five or six years older than he, and she was still very attractive. But she was hard and grasping, not a nice person at all. But then, Katy thought, what do I know? Maybe that didn't matter to men. Maybe they didn't see beyond the blond hair and the carefully made-up face. In any case, it was none of her business.

She tilted her chin proudly. "You're behaving very foolishly, Mrs. Barnett. I have no intention of becoming involved with Trace or any other man."

"And you expect me to believe that?"

"I really don't care what you believe."

"Why you little—" The sound of Trace's footsteps crossing the hall abruptly halted the angry tirade, and Saundra clamped her mouth shut, shooting Katy one last, furious glare.

"Here we are." Trace draped the lacy shawl over Katy's shoulders and placed a hand beneath her elbow.

"Shall we go?" He ignored his stepmother completely, but Katy could feel the woman's eyes boring into her back as she allowed him to lead her from the room.

Outside on the veranda Trace paused. "If you'll wait here, I'll get my car and bring it around."

"No, please. I would really much rather walk."

"Very well. If that's what you want." Trace smiled pleasantly and extended his arm. "Shall we go?"

It was then Katy realized that he intended to walk with her. "Oh, but I meant . . ."

"I know what you meant, Katy," he said softly. "But I also meant it when I said I would see you home. Now, what's it going to be? Do we drive or do we walk?"

Katy looked at him uncertainly in the dim light filtering through the windows, her teeth worrying the soft inner tissue of her bottom lip. She saw the rock-hard determination in his expression and knew she was not going to be able to dissuade him.

She sighed deeply, her shoulders sagging in defeat. "We walk."

Ignoring his arm, she descended the veranda steps and started around the corner of the house to follow the path that led to the stables. Trace fell in step beside her. Katy walked quickly, her chaotic thoughts tumbling over themselves in a jumble of confusion. Her mind groped in frantic desperation for an avenue of escape, but she could not concentrate. Awareness of the tall, vigorous man at her side flooded her senses and her brain simply refused to function.

As they neared the stables, they could hear the mare's nervous whicker. A rectangle of light spilled from one of the stalls at the far end of the row. Katy heard her father's voice, crooning encouragement to the frightened animal, his tone low and soothing, the words unintelligible.

Green Acres Farm rarely called in the local veterinarian. They didn't need him. Not when they had Tom Donovan. But perhaps Trace didn't know that.

Katy looked up at him. "If you feel you should be there, Mr. Barnett, please don't worry about me. I assure you I can find my way home alone with no problem."

He grasped her upper arm and began to lead her past the row of stalls. "Give it up, Katy. It won't work. I'll check the progress at the stables later, but right now I intend to walk you home. So no more arguing."

Behind the stables the road wound through a small stand of trees, and when they entered it, they were immediately enclosed in almost total darkness. Katy's heart began to thud painfully. You fool! You utter fool! Why did you insist upon walking? she berated herself silently. It would have taken no more than five minutes to get home by car. Instead, here she was, walking along a dark, country road with a man who terrified her.

A thick layer of pine needles carpeted the dirt road, muffling the sound of their footsteps. As quiet as it was, their approach startled a small, nocturnal creature, and it scurried deeper into the woods, amid a frantic rustle of brush. From nearby came the low, mournful hoot of an owl. The small sounds added to the feeling of complete isolation, and Katy felt gooseflesh rise along her arms. She shivered and drew the shawl closer to her body.

"Are you cold?"

The sharp question gave her a start. "What? Oh . . . no . . . that is . . ." The days were now pleasantly warm, but the early spring nights still held a biting chill. It had nothing to do with her reaction, but it provided a convenient excuse. "It's just a little cooler than I thought it would be."

The hand that gripped her elbow slid up her arm, and she shivered again. "You *are* cold. Here, wear my coat."

"No, I couldn't . . ." she began, but before she could

stop him, Trace had shrugged out of his suit coat and draped it across her shoulders.

"There, that should help."

"But now you'll be cold," Katy protested. She didn't want to wear his coat. It was still warm from the heat of his body, and smelled faintly of tobacco and aftershave. She felt suffocated in the engulfing, wide-shouldered garment. It was almost like being held in his arms.

"Don't worry about me. I've been living in the high country for the last four years. I'm used to the cold."

"The high country? Where is that?" she asked cautiously. The question was not prompted by curiosity, but by a desperate hope that conversation would dispel the intimacy which seemed to surround them.

"Colorado. I bummed around for a time after I left the farm, then I ran into an old friend. One of my college buddies. To make a long story short, we ended up going into the ranching business together. Using a part of my inheritance from my grandmother, along with what Hank had been able to scrape together over the years, we bought a small spread, fifty head of cattle, and a good seed bull." He laughed softly. "It's been an uphill struggle all the way, but now our herd is considerably larger and we're finally beginning to show a profit."

Katy held her breath for a minute, then asked the question that was tormenting her. "Are you going to go back?"

The road opened suddenly into the meadow. In the weak, silvery light of a crescent moon, Katy saw Trace's mouth curve with ironic amusement. "No. At least, not for a while. And then probably just on flying visits."

He looked up at the dark, velvet sky, his eyes skimming over the bright clusters of stars. "When I got the call from our family attorney about Dad's death I came here intending to stay only long enough to attend the funeral and pick up the remainder of my personal belongings." He looked down at Katy and shrugged his broad shoulders, smiling. "I think I was more surprised than anyone to learn that Dad had left the farm to me. I suppose he finally suffered an attack of conscience."

"Well, after all, you *are* his son."

"Yes, I am that." He sighed wearily. "But I think the real reason he did it was because I'm my mother's son. You see, it was her money that saved the farm." Katy's start of surprise drew a bark of bitter laughter from Trace. "As I understand it, my grandfather was a very poor business man with very extravagant tastes. By the time my father inherited the place, it was mortgaged to the hilt. So . . . he married my mother. Her family had just struck it rich in the oil business, and with their help he was able to get the farm back on its feet and recoup the family fortune, even increase it. Unfortunately, he was never able to forgive my mother for being one of that contemptible breed known as the nouveau riche, a group of upstarts with no pedigree to speak of. It seemed to embarrass him." He paused, then continued bitterly, "I remember waking up one night to hear them quarreling. He took great delight in telling her he'd never loved her, that she was socially inferior, and he would never have married her if it hadn't been for her money." His voice hardened and deepened. "After that she was never the same."

Katy was horrified. Temporarily her fear of Trace was forgotten, submerged under a huge, engulfing wave of compassion and pity, something she had never expected to feel for this man. It was difficult for her even to imagine growing up in such a cold, bitter environment. The love that had existed between her mother and father was warm and deep and constant. Katy had grown up secure in the knowledge that she was the wanted and cherished result of that love.

In the pale light of the moon Trace's expression was

cold and formidable. How awful it must have been for him. He had adored his mother, that much she remembered. Was that why he had rebelled so against his father? Was his wildness, his open defiance, Trace's way of fighting back, of striking out at the man who had hurt her? It was possible. Still, it had nothing to do with her.

"You really shouldn't be telling me all this, Mr. Barnett. It's none of my business." She preferred to keep their relationship an impersonal one, the way it had always been. If he persisted in telling her the intimate details of his childhood and his parents' marriage she couldn't do that.

"I want you to know, Katy. I want you to understand," Trace said softly.

They had reached the house, and shrugging off his hand, Katy turned and walked quickly up the brick path to the porch. "I do understand. Believe me, I won't again make the mistake of assuming you share your father's opinions and values." Rummaging through her purse for the house key as she climbed the steps, Katy was extremely conscious of Trace walking beside her, his eyes on her down-bent head.

At the door, without warning, his hands descended on her upper arms and he turned her around. Instinctively, Katy hunched her shoulders forward and tried to pull free of his hold, but found herself trapped between the door and Trace's hard body. She raised frightened eyes to search his face. A silent plea shimmered in their blue depths. She had left a light burning in the living room, and from the soft glow spilling onto the porch, she could just make out his expression. It held a strange mixture of tenderness and determination, with just a touch of impatience.

"Oh, Katy. How long are you going to ignore it?" he asked softly, his voice edged with exasperation.

The feel of his warm hands on her shoulders was so

unnerving that she could barely concentrate on his words. She shook her head as if to clear it and stared at him, transfixed. "Ignore what?"

"This thing there is between us."

Alarm bells began to clang in her head. "I—I don't know what you're talking about."

He gave her a little shake. "Stop it, Katy. You're as aware of me as I am of you. Don't deny it." Lifting one hand, he ran his knuckles gently down her cheek. "It started four years ago. I wanted you then, very much, but you were so young and so painfully shy, I knew I had to wait. Then I quarreled with my father. At the time I was grateful nothing had developed between us, because I couldn't stay after that." His voice dropped to a low, husky pitch, while his eyes burned possessively over her frightened face. "When I looked up and saw you at my father's funeral, all those feelings I had four years ago came rushing back, only stronger this time. I'd made up my mind to stay, even before I knew I had inherited the farm. I wasn't going to let you slip through my fingers again."

Wide-eyed, Katy stared at him. She shook her head wordlessly, feeling the familiar, cold fear unfurl itself deep inside her. It was happening all over again. This man wanted her. He admitted it openly. And he seemed to think all he had to do was reach out and take her, that she would accept that, even be pleased. That he could even think such a thing filled her with a deep sense of shame and humiliation. What was there about her that made men think she was theirs for the taking like some pretty toy? It was so unfair! She wanted to cry and rage at the same time.

"You don't know what you're saying!" she cried desperately. "There's nothing between us! There never has been and there never will be! So why don't you just leave me alone?"

"Oh, no, Katy," he said quietly, determinedly. "I'm

not going to let you hide behind that pathetic little shell you've built around yourself. I've tried to be patient with you, to let you get used to having me around, and it's gotten me absolutely nowhere. Well, no more." He pulled her close, and Katy's hands came up to push him away, but it was useless. His arms slid around her back and tightened, molding her slender body to his hard one, her soft breasts crushed against the muscular wall of his chest.

Katy's first instinct was to fight. She wanted desperately to lash out and claw and kick, to inflict as much injury as possible, but she had learned, to her sorrow, that that was not the way to handle an explosive situation. Instead, she held herself rigid. Like a tethered animal watching the approach of a hungry predator, she stood perfectly still, her eyes huge in her white face, as Trace's head began its slow, purposeful descent.

"No, please don't," she whispered helplessly, and heard him give a soft laugh an instant before his lips settled over hers.

It was a tantalizing kiss, soft and gentle, and infinitely sensual. He explored her lips with a controlled passion that made no demands, yet established, beyond a doubt, his absolute possession. Katy was stunned by the complete lack of brutality in his lovemaking. It was something she had expected, had braced herself for, and its absence left her confused and disoriented. She felt weak. Boneless.

Trace's mouth moved unhurriedly over her lips, persuasively teasing and nibbling at their trembling softness until they parted without her being aware of it. When the tip of his tongue touched hers, a tingling shaft of excitement streaked through her, and she shuddered violently from head to foot. Feeling her reaction, Trace ended the kiss. He drew his mouth slowly from hers and smiled down at her bewildered face.

"You see. That wasn't so bad, was it?" he mocked gently.

Numb with shock, and something else she couldn't even attempt to define, Katy could only stare at him. She was weak and shaken, and knew, vaguely, that her condition was not due entirely to fear.

Trace cupped her face in his hands and ran his thumb over her parted lips. A searing blaze leaped in his eyes as he watched them tremble beneath his touch. Regretfully, he let his hands slide down to curve around her shoulders and dragged his gaze away from the sweet temptation of her mouth. Katy's heart turned over at the virile, passionate look in his eyes as they roamed over her face. "I may as well tell you right now, Katy me darlin'. I mean to have you. And nothing you can do or say is going to alter that."

He lowered his head once more and bestowed a swift, hard kiss, then took the key from her nerveless hand and opened the door. "Now, go to bed, Katy. I'll see you tomorrow." A hand in the small of her back gently pushed her inside, then the door was closed behind her.

It was only as she stood, stock still, in the middle of the living room, listening to the sound of his receding footsteps, that she realized his coat was still draped over her shoulders.

Chapter Four

Warm spring sunshine caressed Katy's face as she paused on the church steps. Usually she came away from the Sunday morning services with a feeling of tranquillity and peace. But not today. The scene with Trace the night before had left her so upset she couldn't concentrate on anything else. She had gone through the religious rites by rote, her emotions in turmoil, her mind a million miles away.

Pulling the lacy scarf from her head, Katy slipped it into her purse, then stepped to one side and watched the crowd of worshipers file by. She was in no hurry, because she had absolutely nowhere to go. With Trace's "I'll see you tomorrow" still ringing in her ears she didn't dare go home. Katy descended the shallow steps and started slowly toward her car. She had to find something to keep her occupied, something that would keep her away from the house all day. But what?

She was still asking herself the same question as she eased the car out of the parking lot and turned in the direction opposite to the farm. It was hot and stuffy in the car and Katy rolled down her window and opened the vents. Immediately the heavenly scent of roses swirled around her. She breathed deeply and let her eyes wander over the vast rose fields lining the highway on either side. They were just coming into first bloom, acre upon acre of almost every variety and color of rose grown. It was a source of great pride to most Tyler residents that their east Texas town was known as the rose capital of the world. More than half the field-grown rose bushes in the United States came from the immediate vicinity. From April to October the rose fields, which virtually surrounded the town, were a riot of color and scent. To Katy there was no more beautiful sight.

A sign pointing to Tyler lake drew her attention and, with a shrug, Katy decided it was as good a place as any in which to while away a Sunday afternoon.

Spying a fast food restaurant just ahead, she flipped on the turn indicator and swung into the drive-through lane. A few minutes later she pulled back onto the highway, a sack containing a juicy cheeseburger and a large, icy Coke on the seat beside her. The appetizing aroma filling the car made her nose twitch apprecia-tively.

At the lake Katy drove around the shore until she found a secluded picnic table among the towering pine trees. She parked her car in the space provided and carried her lunch to the table. Insects scattered before her, clicking noisily as she walked through the ankle-high grass. Overhead, a family of bluejays flitted through the pines, scolding angrily.

A gentle wind ruffled the surface of the lake, sending tiny wavelets lapping against the shore. Sunlight spar-kled on the rippled water like thousands of glittering diamonds. Far from shore a lone sailboat leaned before the wind, its sail billowed and full, a taut red triangle against the blue of lake and sky. Katy propped her elbows on the picnic table and nibbled on her cheese-burger, watching the scene abstractedly.

It was pure cowardice, running away from Trace like this, but she didn't care. She wasn't ready to face the confrontation that had to come. First she had to talk to her father. He would make Trace understand that she wasn't interested, that he was wasting his time. He *had* to.

There had been no opportunity to speak to her father that morning however. He had come staggering in at dawn, exhausted by his night-long vigil at the stables. After a mumbled greeting he had fallen into bed and, within minutes, had sunk into a deep sleep. His heavy, rumbling snore had followed her as she tiptoed out of the house.

Katy's musings were interrupted by the arrival of a mother duck. A slow smile curved her mouth as she watched the haughty, feathered female waddle imperiously toward the lake, emitting a constant stream of querulous quacks and trailing behind her a wavering line of downy yellow ducklings. As she led her entourage by the table, she eyed Katy as though daring her to move and proceeded toward her destination at the same majestic pace. Reaching the lake, she waded a few feet into the shallows, then lowered her body with a plopping splash and glided gracefully away. One after the other, the bits of yellow fluff followed suit, paddling effortlessly in their mother's wake.

Katy drank the last of her Coke and tossed the cup in the trash barrel, then picked up the remainder of her cheeseburger and wandered down to the shore. She laughed as she watched the mother duck dive in search of food, leaving only her feathered rump sticking out of the water, straight up in the air. Clicking her tongue, Katy tore off small pieces of bun and tossed them into the water. Immediately the ducks snapped up the crumbs of bread eagerly and when they were gone, swam toward the shore and audaciously demanded more. Katy laughed aloud and obliged. She watched them scrabbling after the scattered tidbits with a certain amount of envy, thinking wistfully how uncomplicated their lives were compared to hers.

When the bun was gone, Katy wandered along the

shore. The ducks followed hopefully for a while, then turned back in disgust when it became apparent there would be no more handouts. The breeze off the lake rustled the pine needles overhead as Katy strolled aimlessly along. She couldn't understand why Trace upset her so, but he did. After all, he couldn't force her into a relationship she didn't want. Several men had made a dead set at her before, and she had simply ignored them. So why couldn't she ignore Trace? The question was unanswerable, but one thing she knew for certain. Trace affected her like no other man ever had, and that alone frightened her. She didn't like the sensations he aroused—the fluttering in the pit of her stomach; the slow, heavy thud of her heart; the weak, watery feeling that threatened to buckle her knees. Troubled, Katy trudged on, wrestling with the problem for almost an hour before finally turning back.

It was only a little after three when she climbed into the car and headed toward Tyler, much too early to go home. The only other place she could think of to go was Jane and Frank's.

It wasn't until she had already rung the Cawleys' doorbell that the first pangs of doubt began to nag at her. Jane was as sharp as a tack. Katy wasn't in the habit of dropping by on the weekends, and Jane was bound to wonder why she had today. The bell pealed inside the house several times without any answer, and feeling something akin to relief, Katy turned to go. Before she had taken two steps the door was jerked open.

"Katy! Well, this is a surprise. What are you doing here?"

Katy turned and smiled. "Oh, I was just at loose ends and I thought I'd see if you were busy."

"No. Of course not." Jane stepped back and opened the door wide. "Come in, come in. Everyone is out back around the pool. Come on out and join us."

Katy hung back. "Maybe I'd better not. I don't want to interrupt your Sunday with your family."

"Nonsense!" Jane reached out and grabbed her by the arm. "There's no reason in the world why you can't join us. As I recall, you left one of your swimsuits in the pool house the last time you were here. Besides, we all think of you as a member of the family anyway."

Frank and the kids were in the pool playing a game of catch with a beach ball when Katy and Jane stepped out onto the patio. They paused just long enough to chorus a quick "Hi, Katy," before returning to the game, playing fast and furious, as though their very lives depended on the outcome. The Cawleys' fifteen-year-old twins, John and Jason, were on one side, teamed against Frank and seventeen-year-old Martha on the other.

"Good grief! It makes me tired just to watch them. How do you keep up with this crew?" Katy asked as she sank down onto a padded lounger.

"It isn't easy, believe me." Jane sighed and plopped down on another lounger. Arms stretched out behind her, she leaned back on her hands, then turned her head and gave Katy an inquiring look, her brown eyes narrowing shrewdly. "So, tell me. What happened at the farm to send you scurrying into town?" she asked with typical directness.

"Nothing." Katy kept her eyes on the game of catch and avoided looking at her friend. "It's just that Dad was up all night with an ailing horse, and he's exhausted. I thought I'd stay away from the house and give him a chance to catch up on his sleep."

"Mmmm, and that's all there is to it, huh?"

"Yes, of course. What else could there be?"

"What else, indeed." Jane sniffed. "Only the most eligible, best-looking man in the county, that's all. And don't sit there and give me that big-eyed look. I know perfectly well that Trace Barnett is involved in this somehow."

"Of course he's involved. It was his ailing horse."

"Katy Donovan! Don't try to con me. I know good and . . ."

"Hey, Katy!" Jason called from the edge of the pool. "Why don't you get into your swimsuit and you and Mom join us? We'll have a three-man relay. Girls against the boys. What do you say?"

Katy grabbed at the chance to escape Jane's inquisition. Jumping up, she headed for the poolhouse. "Sure. Just give me five minutes," she called as she skirted the pool. "We gals are going to beat the pants off you, you'll see."

A feeling of intense relief washed over Katy when she arrived home and turned into the empty drive. Though it was after nine, she had half expected to find Trace's pickup parked next to the house, but there wasn't a vehicle of any kind in sight. She relaxed and drove around to the back where she parked the car next to her father's pickup.

She smiled as she climbed from the car and started toward the house on slightly unsteady legs. She was feeling pleasantly exhausted by the afternoon and evening spent with the irrepressible Cawley clan. They had played water games until hunger had forced them to call a halt. Then, among a storm of unmerciful teasing and lighthearted squabbling, they had grilled hot dogs over the barbeque pit and stuffed themselves like ravenous wolves.

Katy had stayed as long as she had dared without raising Jane's suspicions any further. But by nine, after all the mess had been cleared away and the children had wandered off, Jane once again began to ask probing questions, and Katy had beat a hasty retreat.

A long rectangle of yellow light spilling from the kitchen lit her way as Katy climbed the back steps and opened the door to the screened-in utility porch. The soft tap-tap of her heels on the board floor announced her arrival even before she called out, "Hi, Dad. I'm back."

"Katy me darlin'! It's about time you were home," her father answered from the living room. "Where the devil have you been all day?"

"Most of the time I've been at the Cawleys'. We swam and pla . . ." The words froze on Katy's lips, and she came to a stunned halt just inside the living room as her eyes lit on the long, lean man sprawled in one of the fireside chairs. His narrowed stare seemed to slice right through her as she stood rooted to the spot.

"Trace! Wh-what are you doing here?"

"He came to see you, my girl. Trace was under the impression you were expecting him."

There was a gruffness in her father's voice that Katy hadn't noticed before, and when she turned to him and saw his reddened, bleary eyes and disheveled appearance her heart sank. He had been drinking again. Heavily.

"I—I—must have forgotten. I—"

"Don't worry about it, Tom." Trace cut into her stammered explanation and sent her a knowing look that made her scalp prickle. "I probably didn't make my intentions clear last night." He paused and a slow grin curved his mouth. "That's a mistake I won't make in the future, I assure you."

The softly spoken words hit Katy with stunning impact, and she took a step backward, reeling under the implied threat. Her breathing was shallow, her chest tight. Cold, icy fear was racing through her veins. Her eyes darted to her father, but he seemed sublimely unperturbed, his gaze trained on the glass in his hand.

Trace stood up, and Katy jumped. Her involuntary reaction brought his brows together.

"Is anything wrong, Katy? You seem . . ." he paused, his eyes narrowing on her white face, "nervous."

It was a politely worded question but Katy didn't

miss the thread of steel in his voice. It made her even more nervous. She didn't want him probing for the cause. The fewer people who knew, the better.

Forcing a smile to her lips, she shook her head. "No. Of course not. I'm just tired, that's all."

"I see," he said thoughtfully. "In that case, I'll be going." He picked up his hat and gave her father a grim smile. "Tom, I'll see you in the morning."

Katy sagged with relief. She followed him happily as he headed for the door, barely able to believe she was getting rid of him so easily. Her deliverance was short-lived however. At the door he grasped her elbow and sent Tom an inquiring look. "You don't mind if Katy walks me to the gate, do you, Tom? I'd like to speak with her for a moment."

"Sure, sure." Tom waved his hand dismissively. "You two go on. Me, I'm going to bed." So saying, he rose to his feet and staggered toward the hall door. Wide-eyed, Katy watched his retreating back with something akin to panic.

"Oh, but . . ."

Her protest was cut off as Trace transferred his hand from her elbow to the small of her back, its forward pressure propelling her through the open door. Without engaging in an undignified struggle, she had no choice but to go with him.

Katy walked stiffly beside him. The pressure of that guiding hand on her back was burning through her clothing like a branding iron. She was shivering with reaction to this frighteningly masculine man, a combination of fear, anger and resentment, and had no doubt that he could feel the tremors that quaked through her.

At the gate he stopped and turned her to face him. Partly out of fear and partly out of sheer stubbornness, Katy kept her eyes fixed firmly on the third button of his shirt. His first words, however, brought her head up sharply, her eyes widening in dismay.

"How long has Tom been drinking like this, Katy?"

In the pale glow of light from the house she couldn't see his expression clearly. She looked at him with huge, stricken eyes, searching his face for some sign of compassion or understanding. Oh, dear God! Don't let him dismiss Dad, she prayed fervently. Not now. Not after everything else. Please, God, please!

Her gaze wavered beneath his penetrating stare, and Katy lowered her head. Her soft lips trembled as she whispered huskily, agonizingly, "Ever since Mother died. You see . . . he loved her so, he can't bear to go on without her. It's killing him, little by little, day by day." The last was choked out on a rising sob, and she averted her head, blinking rapidly to hold back the tears that threatened. Katy's chin quivered as she fought to suppress the emotions churning inside her. Her throat ached with the effort.

Trace drew in a deep breath and expelled it very slowly, in a long, resigned sigh. "That's what I thought," he said, his tone grim. "I've noticed he doesn't seem the same as I remembered him, even sober."

"No, he's not. When Mother died, something in him died too. Some vital spark." Katy stood with her arms crossed over her midriff, rubbing her elbows in agitation. "He's . . ."

Tom's deep, rich baritone, raised in song, halted Katy's words. They both turned to stare at the house, unable to speak as a hauntingly sad song floated out on the still night air.

The piercing sorrow in her father's voice snapped the precarious control Katy had over her emotions, and huge, scalding tears welled up to blur her vision. Biting her lips, she widened her eyes and tried to hold them back, but it was no use. One by one, they trickled over.

She turned to Trace then, clutching desperately at his arm, her tear-drenched eyes unconsciously beseeching. "Trace, please. He never drinks during working hours. I swear it! You've got to believe me!"

At first her desperate pleading seemed to shock him. Then a look of pure anguish flickered across his face. "Oh, Katy, Katy," Trace breathed sadly, cupping her face between his hands. Rough, calloused thumbs brushed back and forth across her cheeks, wiping away the steady flow of tears. "Do you really think I would dismiss your father? Do you have so little faith in me? Right now Tom is like a wounded animal, and he's easing his pain in the only way he knows how. I can't condemn him for that."

Katy stood rigid before him, blinking her eyes to stem the tears, staring at him in growing wonder. She could scarcely believe what she was hearing.

A dejected look entered the hazel eyes and Trace shook his head sorrowfully. "Katy, don't you know that Tom has always been more of a father to me than my natural father? It was Tom who bailed me out of trouble countless times during that period when I was behaving like a reckless fool. It was Tom who gave me good, sound advice. It was Tom who understood how I felt." He paused and darted a look toward the house, then sent her that lopsided smile, and Katy's heart gave a queer little lurch against her ribs. "Anyway, I'm not stupid. Tom knows and handles animals better than any man alive, drunk or sober. So don't worry, Katy. I'm not going to dismiss your father just because he's hitting the bottle. We simply have to give him time and hope he eventually snaps out of it."

The rush of gratitude she felt almost overwhelmed her. The vivid blue eyes were swimming with emotion as she looked at him, her chin wobbling. "Thank you, Trace," she whispered unsteadily.

His face became pensive and he stared at the house again. "I know losing her was a terrible blow, but still, it must be wonderful to share that kind of love." The wistful longing in his voice was unmistakable, and something deep inside her stirred. His gaze swung back to Katy and he smiled. His fingers slid into the hair at her temples, the calloused skin snagging the silky strands. "And it must be wonderful to grow up surrounded by that kind of love."

"Yes. It is."

"That's what I want for my children," he said with a soft fierceness that tugged at her heart strings. "That's what I'm determined to give them. And myself."

For a moment Katy was able to ignore the caressing movements of his hands. Pity for this man overwhelmed her as she compared his cold, loveless childhood with her own. When she was much younger, she had been envious of Trace, admiring the big house, the high life-style, and all the material things he possessed in such abundance, when all along she had been the lucky one. There had never been a day in her life when she had been made to feel unwanted, never a moment when she hadn't been surrounded by love.

Against her will, she could feel herself softening toward him. As Katy stared into the rugged but somehow vulnerable face, she wanted desperately for Trace to know that kind of deep, abiding love, and her eyes clearly reflected her feelings. "I hope you can, Trace," she said with soft sincerity. "I truly hope you can."

Trace smiled. "Oh, don't worry, sweetheart. I fully intend to. And that brings us back to the original reason for my visit."

He brought his face closer to hers, and Katy's eyes widened with renewed fear. She gripped his wrists and tried to pull back but he tunneled his fingers deeper into her hair and held her immobile. Katy's throat went dry as she met the determined gleam in his eyes.

"You knew I was coming here today to see you, didn't you, Katy?" The question was asked in a pleasant tone that, nevertheless, held a warning challenge, but Trace didn't give her a chance to reply. "I very considerately waited until late afternoon so I wouldn't disturb your father," he continued silkily. "And what do I find when I get here? Katy me darlin' has flown the coop. Well, running away won't do you any good, my love. You won't escape me that easily." His voice went low with warning. "Try it again, and I'll come looking for you."

His fingers tightened against her scalp, forcing her head up. Stunned, shaking with fright, Katy could only stare with huge, stricken eyes as his mouth moved closer, closer. When she felt his warm breath mingle with hers, she uttered a strangled "No!"

It was too late. He brushed a soft kiss against her parted lips, then another, and another—delicate butterfly caresses that sent her blood racing through her veins.

Trace raised his head and smiled down at her. "Good night, Katy." Bending swiftly, he dropped a kiss on the end of her nose. In the next instant he was striding away down the road.

The deafening roar of her heartbeat pounded in Katy's ears as she stared into the darkness that had swallowed him up. How did one fight a man like Trace? His gentle persistence was like the changing seasons, the steady ebb and flow of the tides—a gradual, inexorable force that would not be denied. The thought sent a shiver rippling through her. Hugging herself tightly, Katy stared up at the brilliant pinpoints of light in the sky and drew in several deep breaths. Well, she wouldn't give in to him. She wouldn't!

"Are you sure we can't give you a lift, Katy? It would be no trouble, really."

"Jane's right, Katy," Frank added his support to his wife's offer as the three of them walked down the hall toward the office. "Green Meadows isn't that far. Besides, I'd hardly call a drive into the country on a glorious day like this a hardship."

"Thanks. I appreciate your offer. But Dad said he'd be here at six to pick me up." Katy smiled back over her shoulder at her two friends as they stepped, single file, through the door into the office.

"Well, I just wish you had told us your car would be in the garage for a few days. There's no need for your father to run back and forth like this." Jane stopped in the middle of the room to rummage through her purse and finally extracted a large ring of jangling keys. She opened the door, motioning for the others to go through ahead of her. "If it's not repaired by Monday, just tell him we'll bring you home," she ordered imperiously.

"Yes, mother hen." Laughing, Katy stepped through the outer door, then came to an abrupt halt that sent Frank and Jane skidding into her.

"What the . . ." They had cried out in unison, but the startled exclamation died on their lips at the sight of the tall, sandy-haired man leaning against the wall, just outside the door. Three pairs of rounded eyes stared at him, and Trace smiled back, a hint of devilish amusement in his expression.

"Trace! What are you doing here?" Katy choked out the words through a tightly constricted throat. But even as the question was asked she had a sinking feeling what his answer would be, and her eyes began to dart around in search of her father.

Trace pushed himself away from the wall, closed the distance between them, and slipped his arm around Katy's waist. Before she realized his intent, he lowered his head and gave her a quick kiss on the mouth that unnerved her. While she was trying to gather her scattered wits, he turned and extended his hand to Frank.

"Hello. I'm Trace Barnett," he said pleasantly.

"Frank Cawley," the other man answered with wary caution, accepting the proffered hand. "And this is my wife, Jane."

Katy's heart lurched at the dazed expression on

Jane's face when Trace turned that devastating smile on her.

"You must be Katy's boss. Tom was telling me how much she enjoys working for you. I understand the two of you have become good friends."

"Yes. Yes we have," Jane replied distractedly. "Katy's a dear."

Smiling, Trace looked down at Katy and pulled her closer. Belatedly she became aware of the familiarity of the embrace and tried to pull free, but his fingers bit warningly into the soft flesh of her midriff. "Yes, I quite agree," he concurred in a husky, intimate tone, as his possessive gaze wandered over her. "Very dear."

For a moment Katy could only gape at him. Trace was deliberately trying to give the impression they were romantically involved! She darted an uneasy look at Jane and Frank, and her heart sank all the way to her knees. From their surprised, but very definitely pleased expressions, it was obvious that was exactly what they thought.

"Trace, you can't . . ." she began worriedly, but the muscular arm pressing against her back turned her toward the steps and urged her forward.

He smiled at the startled couple as he guided her past them. "Sorry to run, but I promised Tom I'd bring Katy straight home. Perhaps the four of us can get together soon," he tossed over her shoulder. "I'm anxious to get to know Katy's friends." And with that, he led a shaken Katy swiftly down the walk.

"I'm parked about a block away," he informed her as they reached the city sidewalk and turned right. "When I arrived, the drive in front of the school was filled with waiting mothers, and I didn't feel like joining the queue." He gave her his most beguiling smile. "You don't mind walking, do you?"

But she did mind. She minded very much. It wasn't enough that he had kissed her in front of her friends and given them a totally false impression of their relationship. Now he was leading her down a public street with his arm curved possessively around her waist in full view of the whole town. Several passersby were staring quite openly. Trace Barnett was a well-known figure in this town, and since he had inherited Green Meadows, speculation about him had been running rampant. With a sinking feeling in the pit of her stomach, Katy accepted that news of this little episode would spread like a brush fire.

Just when she thought things couldn't get any worse, she looked up and caught sight of the Whittingdale sisters bearing down on them from the opposite direction. Katy closed her eyes and groaned. The Whittingdale ladies were the nerve center of the Tyler gossip network. Two wealthy spinsters, they lived their lives vicariously through others. Who was doing what with whom was of vital interest to them, and Katy knew they had always found Trace's escapades particularly titillating.

"Trace, will you let me go," she whispered furiously, while desperately trying to dislodge his hand from her waist. "Flora and Irene are coming this way."

"So? Let them come," he answered, with a distressing lack of concern.

"Let me go! What are you trying to do? Ruin my reputation? You know as well as I that if they see us like this, within five minutes they'll have me branded as one of your women."

"Not *one* of my women. My *only* woman."

The calm pronouncement brought her to a jerking halt. Wide, distressed blue eyes searched his face in growing panic. "Wh-what do you mean? What are you trying to do, Trace?" Her voice rose to a shrill pitch when she noticed the smug expression on his face.

The encircling arm was removed from her waist, and he turned her fully toward him, his big hands cupping the curves of her shoulders. Katy was uncomfortably aware of the rapid approach of the Whittingdale sisters, but knew it was useless to fight against the steely hold. She stood staring at him uncertainly.

"It's really very simple, Katy," he drawled with a complacent smile. His hands tightened and he drew her closer. "I'm staking my claim. I'm giving all the other single males fair warning that Mary Kathleen Donovan is spoken for."

The stunning words, the quiet tone, the deadly serious look in his eyes, all combined to send an icy chill trickling down her spine. Automatically, without her even being aware of it, her head began to move from side to side in frantic, insistent denial. And all the time, Trace was drawing her closer. Mute with fear, Katy could only watch helplessly as his head bent slowly toward her. With his lips poised directly over hers, he paused and glanced over her shoulder.

"Good afternoon, ladies," he said pleasantly, when the Whittingdales drew abreast of them. And then, ignoring their scandalized gasps, he lowered his mouth to Katy's.

It was a long, lingering kiss, not brutal, but demanding nevertheless, the insistent pressure of his lips prying hers apart and forcing her to accept his warm, thrusting tongue. Katy writhed beneath the searing kiss and tried vainly to twist away, but Trace slipped his arms around her and pulled her tightly against him. His previous kisses had been brief, fleeting affairs, ending before she'd had time to panic, but now she was suffocating under his devouring male dominance, hysteria boiling up inside her, choking her.

The nightmare was happening all over again. The horrid, vicious pictures flickered through her mind, and she couldn't shut them out. She was being used, humiliated, stripped of her will as though it were of no importance, forced to accept a man's hot, demanding mouth and the insolent touch of his hands, like some worthless, mindless nothing. And she knew only too well that if she resisted, those same hands could turn violent, could hurt her. A dark, black terror gripped her, and Katy began to shiver uncontrollably, her knees buckling.

Helpless tears ran down her face from beneath her closed lids. They trickled against Trace's lips, and when he tasted their salty wetness he broke off the kiss to look down at her. Shock froze his features at the sight of her ghastly pallor.

"Katy! My god! What's wrong?"

She sagged between his hands, her head drooping forward until her chin touched her chest. A dizzying blackness swirled around the edge of her consciousness and her stomach churned. "I . . . I . . . think I'm going to be sick," she whispered weakly.

"No, you're not."

Bending, he scooped her up in his arms and covered the short distance to the car with long, ground-eating strides. Somehow he managed to open the door and thrust her inside. Then his hand was on the back of her neck, pushing her head down between her knees.

"Take deep breaths, Katy, and let them out nice and slowly. That's my girl." He crooned the soothing words as she obeyed. He was squatted down on his haunches beside the open door, bending protectively over her, his hands tender as they stroked the back of her neck and shoulders.

Katy remained bent over for a long time, drawing in deep, reviving gulps of air. Finally her heartbeat slowed, and the dizzying sickness began to fade. She lifted her head and gave him a wan smile. "I—I think I'll be all right now," she said in a weak, quivering voice.

"Are you sure?" Trace very gently cupped her jaw with one hand and scanned her white face. Worry and puzzlement flickered in his eyes.

"Yes. Yes, I'm sure."

Over his shoulder Katy noticed the clutch of people gathered on the sidewalk, gaping at the spectacle she'd provided, and turned her head away sharply, her humiliation deepening. Good Lord! By tonight the story would be all over town.

If the embarrassing situation bothered Trace he certainly didn't let it show. He pulled a handkerchief from his pocket and very tenderly wiped the perspiration from her face, pushing back the disheveled strands of glistening black hair. When finished, he fastened the seat belt around her, stood up and closed the door firmly, then walked around to the other side and slid in behind the wheel. He didn't even glance at the crowd of people on the sidewalk. Pausing briefly, he cast her a quick, assessing look, then flicked the ignition key and pulled away from the curb.

A merciful numbness settled over Katy and she sat huddled against the door, staring out the side window with dry, sightless eyes. The rose fields whizzed by in a long streak of blurred rainbow colors.

"All right, Katy," Trace said quietly, but determinedly. "I think it's time you and I had a serious talk. What happened back there?"

"Nothing. At least, nothing that concerns you," she said with a zombielike flatness. "Just leave me alone, Trace. That's all I ask. Just get out of my life and leave me alone."

"No, Katy. I won't do that. I *can't* do that. Haven't you realized that yet?"

Katy didn't answer him, and after a few minutes he sighed. "Okay. If you're not ready to talk yet, I won't press. But when we get back to the farm we're going to have this out. It's gone on far too long. Something is wrong, and I intend to find out what."

Katy's only answer was a cool, level look. So they were going to have a talk, were they? she thought resentfully. Just like that. Whether she agreed or not. Well, think again, Mr. Trace Barnett.

He didn't look at her, and finally she returned her gaze to the passing scenery. She felt raw and vulnerable, exposed. Trace's very presence scraped against her nerves. Why couldn't he just leave her alone? She'd had her life under control before Trace returned, but somehow he had managed to penetrate her protective shell of indifference. More so today than usual, because his sudden appearance had come as a shock. On Monday he'd flown to Colorado to settle his affairs there, and she had not expected him back so soon.

The car had barely come to a stop in the drive when Katy reached for the door handle. She scrambled out and dashed for the house, but Trace was too fast for her. He moved across the yard like a shot and took the porch steps in one leap. Before she could get the screen door completely open he was beside her, grabbing her arm and shoving the door shut again.

"Oh, no, you don't, Katy. You're not going to run out on me now," he said determinedly.

"Let me go!" she demanded. "You have no rights over me! I'm not part of the farm property!" Katy was fighting for control. She knew if she didn't get away from him soon, she was going to explode. She was hovering on the raw edge of panic, and it would take very little to push her over. Her frayed nerves simply couldn't stand any more strain.

"I never said you were. But for God's sake, Katy! Why won't you tell me what's wrong?"

"Because it's none of your damned business!" she shouted wildly. Twisting her arm free, she snatched at the screen door again, but Trace slammed his hand against it with a splintering force that made the wooden frame tremble.

He grabbed her shoulders and gave her a little shake. "Dammit, Katy, you—"

"What the devil is going on here?" Tom Donovan's massive bulk loomed up on the other side of the screen door. His brows came down in a thunderous scowl as he noticed his daughter's distraught face, and his narrowing gaze swung to the man holding her. "Take your hands off her, Trace," he commanded with quiet menace. "Now."

Defiant anger flared in the hazel eyes as they locked on the older man. A muscle jerked beside the grim line of his mouth, and for a moment Trace looked as though he were about to argue. Then, his jaw tight, he slowly, reluctantly, let his hands fall to his sides and took a step backward.

Pushing open the screen door, Tom stepped out onto the porch and silently gathered Katy into his arms. He held her close, his huge frame absorbing the violent tremors that quaked through her, his rough, paw-like hand tenderly stroking the silky head lying against his chest. He fixed the younger man with a hard, demanding stare. "What did you do to her?"

"I kissed her."

Some of the anger seemed to go out of Tom. "I see," he murmured. Tired gray eyes gazed down at the trembling girl cradled in his arms, and he shook his head sadly. "Well, that explains it."

"What's wrong with her, Tom? And don't tell me she's shy. There's more to this than just shyness. A woman doesn't get sick just because a man kisses her."

Before her father could answer, Katy twisted around. Her blue eyes were icy as she glared at Trace. "I told you it's none of your business! Now please leave me alone."

"I love you, Katy. And I want to marry you," Trace stated flatly. "That makes it my business."

She sucked in a hissing breath and her eyes grew dark, the pupils expanding until there was only a thin ring of blue around the outer edges. "You can't be serious," she breathed out shakily. "I'm not going to marry you! I'm not going to marry anyone!"

Trace held her terror-stricken gaze for a moment, then looked at her father. "I meant what I said, Tom. I love her. I have a right to know."

"Trace, my boy," Tom began doubtfully. "You've

only been back a few weeks. How can you be sure of your feelings so quickly?"

The hazel gaze didn't waver. "How long did it take you to realize that you loved Kathleen?"

Tom's brows rose in mild surprise, then a faraway look entered his eyes, and his craggy features softened. Shaking his head, he gave the younger man a rueful smile. After a tense pause, he heaved a sigh. "All right, Trace. I'll tell you."

Chapter Five

"Dad, no! You can't! I won't let you!" Katy's face lost every vestige of color as she stared up at her father.

"Katy girl, listen to me," Tom urged softly.

"No! No, I won't! You can't . . ."

"Stop it, Katy!"

He grasped her by the shoulders and shook her, then brought his face down to within inches of hers. "Now listen to me, Katy girl. And listen good. Trace is right. Can't you see that? He loves you and wants to marry you. If you refuse, he deserves to know why. If you accept him, he *should* know what happened. Either way, *he has the right to know!*"

Tom's expression grew infinitely sad as he looked down at her frightened face, and his voice dropped to a low, husky pitch. "Oh, Katy, Katy. Don't you understand? This isn't just for Trace. It's for you too. Not once since it happened have you shed a tear, or even spoken of it directly. You keep it all locked up tight inside you and try to pretend it never happened. Well, it *did* happen, Katy, and you're entitled to your tears and anger. Let's bring it all out into the open and let it go. You'll never get over it until you do."

The air on the porch was thick with tension. Katy

could hardly breathe. She didn't want to talk about it. She didn't even want to think about it. But deep down, she knew her father was right. For a long time she simply stared at him, and then, finally, closed her eyes and nodded.

Tom's face relaxed, and he pulled her close. "That's my Katy," he whispered huskily against the top of her head.

By silent agreement, the three of them filed into the house. Katy went directly to the sofa and curled up in the corner. Propping an elbow on the armrest, she pressed her balled fist against her mouth and turned her face away from the two men. Her slender body was quivering with tension.

Trace remained standing and watched Tom pace restlessly in front of the fireplace. When at last he came to an abrupt halt and swung around, his face was stiff and pale.

"About three years ago," he began in a voice that shook with controlled fury, "Katy was attacked by two men."

The bald statement made Trace's body jerk as though he'd been touched with an electric prod. His jaw clenched, and his fists curled into white knuckled fists at his sides. He stared at the older man, his throat working convulsively, and it was several seconds before he could ask the question that hovered in the air. "Did they . . ."

"No!" Tom answered quickly, shutting off the dreadful word. "No, not that. Thank God." Katy's soft crying made him wince, but he gritted his teeth and went on. "They had dragged her into the woods, but your father and I were returning from town and we heard her screams. We got there in time to prevent . . ." He closed his eyes and waved away the rest of the statement. "But she'd fought them and they had hit her. By the time we arrived she was unconscious." Tom's face contorted with remembered pain and anguish, and he turned away sharply, unable to continue.

"Who were they?" Trace demanded through his teeth.

Tom's face twisted with bitterness as he looked back over his shoulder. "They were guests here at the farm."

"What were their names?"

"I don't know."

"What the hell do you mean, you don't know?! Weren't they prosecuted?"

"No."

"*No?* Didn't they receive *any* punishment?" Trace demanded incredulously. "Didn't you at least give them the beating they deserved?"

Tom braced both arms against the fireplace mantel and hung his head, dejection in every line of his body. "No," he whispered hoarsely.

"Do you mean you let them get away scot free? You did *nothing?*" The questions came out slowly, menacingly, the low, savage tone chilling.

But Tom had had enough. He swung around and confronted the younger man with blazing eyes. "What do you want from me, lad? Don't you think I wanted to tear them limb from limb for what they'd done to my Katy? Of course I did! But I couldn't. At least, not then. Katy needed medical attention." Tom ran an agitated hand through his white hair. "By the time I got back from town, your father had spirited the two men away," he said grimly. "He said if we tried to prosecute his friends, he'd testify on their behalf. He'd swear in a court of law that Katy had enticed them into the woods. It would have been our word against his."

"And you continued to work for a man like that?" Trace ground out in a seething rage. "My God, man! What happened to that fierce Irish pride?"

"I swallowed it for once in my life!" Tom roared back. "And believe me, it was a bitter pill. Look at me, lad. *Look* at me! I'm sixty-three years old. Who's going to hire an old man like me? I had a wife who needed constant medical attention. What choice did I have but to stay?"

Trace looked like a wild man. His eyes were two glittering slits of green fire. His jaw was clenched in anger, and a muscle jumped spasmodically in his cheek. He looked ready to explode.

Swearing violently, he swung around and brought his fist down hard on the back of a chair in a fit of frustrated rage. He stood with his back to the other two, his big frame shaking as he fought for control.

Katy was crying openly now. Wordlessly Tom sat down beside her and gathered her into his arms once again. Her deep, wrenching sobs tore at him, and he laid his cheek against the top of her head, his face ravaged with pain, as the silent tears squeezed from beneath his tightly closed lids.

The three remained that way for a long time, no one daring to move, until finally, finally, the weeping gave way to a series of jarring hiccups, and Katy sat up and wiped her wet cheeks with the back of her hand.

The movement seemed to release Trace from his frozen stance, and he turned slowly. He took a step forward, then stopped when she flinched away from him.

"Katy . . . I—I don't know what to say. Words can't express how sorry I am . . . or how ashamed I am of my father's part in what happened. I know that doesn't help but . . ." He gestured weakly with his hand, then let it fall back to his side.

Katy's chin trembled as she looked down at her hands. Her fingers worked nervously at the skirt of her blue cotton sundress, creasing the material into tiny pleats. She pressed her lips together, unable to speak.

"But, Katy, none of this changes anything," Trace rushed on urgently. "I love you, and I want to marry you. I—"

"No! Don't say that! For God's sake, don't say that! Just leave me alone!" she cried as she turned and buried her face against her father's chest.

"Katy . . ." Trace took another step toward her but Tom held up his hand and shook his head.

"No, Trace. Not now, lad. Not now," he cautioned softly. "Let her be. She's had enough for one day."

Helpless frustration tightened Trace's muscles, and for a moment he looked as though he were going to ignore the command. He stared at Katy's huddled figure for a long time, then sighed and nodded reluctantly. "All right. I won't say any more. But I'll be back."

The screen door banged against its frame as the heavy thud of boots hammered across the wooden porch. Then there was only silence.

Tom unfolded the newspaper, turned a page, then refolded it with a snap. The dry, rustling sound drew Katy's attention, and she looked up from the magazine she was reading. A tender expression settled over her features as she watched her father, scowling at the newspaper through the reading glasses perched on the end of his nose. He was such a *good* man, and so extraordinarily patient with her.

Not once since Trace had stormed out yesterday had he even mentioned the discussion or the traumatic events of three years ago. He had said his piece and brought it all out in the open. Now, how she handled it was up to her. She knew without asking that she would always have his love and support, and, if she wanted it, his advice, but he would push no more. Yesterday, when he had insisted upon telling Trace the whole sordid story, had been one of the few times he had ever pressed her into something against her will.

Katy's gaze returned to the magazine in her lap, and she idly turned another page. Her eyes were slightly out of focus as she stared at the phony, professional smile of the girl in the toothpaste ad. As usual he had been right. Listening to him tell that awful story had been difficult, painfully so, but the long overdue tears had been a catharsis. Three years of built up tension, fear, and anger had been purged from her system, and when her hiccuping sobs had finally ceased, she had felt drained, both physically and emotionally. At her father's insistence she had gone directly to bed and had fallen immediately into the deep oblivion of exhausted sleep. When she awoke this morning she had felt more at peace than she had in years. The business with Trace wasn't over yet, she was aware of that. But perhaps now that he knew the reason for her attitude he would accept her rejection of him.

So immersed was she in her thoughts that she didn't hear the soft fall of footsteps across the porch. When the knock sounded she jumped, her eyes flying to the door.

Her father lowered his newspaper and gave her a quick, concerned glance, then tossed it aside and rose from his chair to answer the summons.

"Good evening, Trace."

"Tom."

A hinge squeaked noisily in the tense silence as the screen door was opened, then closed. Katy felt Trace's presence in the room as surely as if he had touched her. The changing sound of footsteps told her that the two men had left the hardwood floor and were crossing the braided rug, but she kept her eyes on the blurred image in the magazine.

"I know you're here to see Katy, so why don't I just make myself scarce for a bit," Tom offered politely.

Katy's head jerked up, but before she could open her mouth to protest, Trace was speaking.

"No, don't go, Tom. I think it would be best if you both hear what I have to say."

"Very well, lad. If that's what you want." Tom extended his hand toward the other fireside chair. "Have a seat, then."

Katy's heart was beating against her ribs like a newly caged bird as she watched Trace lower his long frame into the chair facing hers. Leaning forward, he placed his elbows on his knees and trained his eyes on the faded, work-stained Stetson that his hands were restlessly turning. Then, without warning, he looked up, straight into Katy's eyes.

"Will you marry me, Katy?" he asked with a curious, dull flatness.

She stared at him for a moment, knocked off balance by the suddenness of his question, then, swallowing hard, turned her head aside. "I—I'm sorry, Trace. I . . . can't," she stammered painfully.

There was a moment of thick silence, then he expelled his breath in a heavy sigh. "That's what I thought you'd say."

Katy looked back at him, drawn by the grimness of his tone. "I can't!" she said more urgently. "Surely you can see that?"

"No, Katy. It's not that you can't, but that you won't. Unless you're forced to."

"Don't be silly." She laughed nervously. "You can't force someone to marry you."

"Can't I?" His eyes bored into her with hard determination and, strangely, what appeared to be regret.

"No. No, of course not," she asserted with more conviction than she felt. She had the strangest sensation that control of the situation was rapidly slipping from her hands.

He looked at her for a long time, the hazel eyes narrowed and intent, then asked blandly, "Tell me, Katy, where do you think your father got the money to pay your mother's medical bills?"

Whatever she had expected him to say, that was not

it, and she blinked in surprise. "Why, I suppose he borrowed it from the bank. Why do you ask?"

"Because the money didn't come from the bank. It came from the operating capital of this farm. Week by week, over a period of several years, your father borrowed what in total amounts to well over twenty-five thousand dollars." He paused to let that sink in, then added softly, chillingly, "They were unauthorized loans, Katy."

Her breath hissed through her tight throat, and for a moment she could only stare at him. Then her incredulous gaze swung to her father.

"Is this true, Dad?"

"I'm afraid it is," he admitted regretfully.

"But—but why? *Why?*"

"If there had been any other way, I would've taken it. But the banks wouldn't loan me the money. They all said I was too old, and the amount was too great. I asked Henry Barnett for a loan, but he turned me down flat. So I took what I needed. It wasn't difficult. Henry never bothered to give the books more than a cursory glance. As long as the farm was showing a healthy profit, he was happy." Tom paused, then his voice hardened. "I'm sorry I had to do it that way, but I would've taken money from St. Peter himself to ease my Kathleen's last days."

A feeling of utter despair engulfed Katy as the seriousness of her father's actions began to penetrate. She rubbed shaking fingers across her forehead and closed her eyes. "Oh, Dad. What have you done?" she murmured helplessly.

"If I had been here, I would have given your father the money, Katy. I hope you believe that. I think you should know, also, that he's been paying the money back in regular monthly installments," Trace said quietly, and Katy's eyes flew open.

"Does that mean you're not going to prosecute

him?" she asked, her face alive with hopeful expectancy.

Pain flickered in the hazel eyes. "No, I'm not going to prosecute."

The moment the words were said, Katy slumped back in the chair, nearly faint with relief, but the reprieve was short lived. His next words hit her like a spray of buckshot.

"But if you won't marry me, I'm going to have to dismiss your father."

"No! You can't mean that! You'll get your money back. Dad will keep up the payments and—and now that I know, I can help," she cried desperately. "That way it will be paid back twi—"

"It isn't the money, Katy," Trace interrupted in a flat, hard voice that stopped her cold.

Her confusion was evident, and seeing it, he continued in a softer, more caressing tone. "I love you, Katy. If I can't have you as my wife, I don't think I could bear to see you every day, to know that you were here at the cottage, just a few hundred yards away, yet completely out of my reach."

"The lad's right." Her father spoke up before Katy could voice the protest on the tip of her tongue. "I know how he feels. If you aren't going to marry him, then we must move on."

"But . . . Dad! You love this place!"

"Aye, that I do. And I'd hoped to live out my days here. But if we must go, we must." She started to speak but he held up his hand and cut her off. "No, Katy. I sympathize with Trace wholeheartedly. Had your mother refused to marry me I couldn't have borne to see her every day. It would be an act of cruelty to stay, and I have too much respect and admiration for Trace to be a party to that."

Stunned, Katy stared at her father, barely able to breathe. A frightening sensation of utter helplessness began to seep into her, penetrating to the very marrow of her bones, and she felt her stomach muscles twist into a hard knot. There was no way out but one, and her mind shied violently away from the thought. If her father lost this job, he would never find another, at least, not one that would pay well enough for him to handle the enormous mountain of debt that loomed over them. And certainly her own meager salary would be of little help. She loved her father dearly and would do anything to help him . . . but to marry Trace, to live intimately with him. . . . A steel door clanged shut in her mind, blocking out the frightful images, and Katy closed her eyes, her body shuddering in remembered terror.

"Katy, listen to me."

Trace's voice came from close at hand, and when she opened her eyes, she found him crouched in front of her chair, his hands braced on either armrest. Instinctively, she shrank back into the cushions. His nearness was oppressive. Katy could feel the heat from his body, smell the clean, male scent of him. His earthy masculinity was a powerful force that wrapped itself around her, making her acutely aware of her own fragile femininity as no other man ever had.

Her reaction brought a quick thinning of his mouth, but Trace pressed on doggedly. His eyes locked with hers, and Katy felt her mouth go dry. She tried to look away, but there was an earnest plea in the green depths that held her mesmerized.

"Katy, I promise you, I give you my solemn word, if you accept my proposal, the marriage will not be consummated until you are ready."

Surprise flickered in her eyes. "You—you mean it would be a marriage in name only?" she asked, her expression guarded.

Wry amusement tugged at the corners of his mouth as his head moved from side to side. "No, Katy. This will be no marriage of convenience," he stated unequivocally. "I love you, and I want very much to make love to you, and I'm confident I shall one day, but not until it's what you want also. I promise I'll not force you or seduce you. You have my word on that. But I reserve the right to do everything in my power to make you want me too. However, you will be in complete control. When our marriage becomes a real one it will be at your request."

Katy noted his use of the word *when* instead of *if*, and silently marveled at his self-confidence. How could he be so positive? And why would he want to take such a risk? She glanced instinctively toward her father, seeking his advice, but his face remained unreadable. Her gaze swung back to the man crouched at her feet. A worried frown creased her delicate brow. "Trace . . . what if that never happens?"

"That's my problem, Katy. Not yours. All you have to do is trust me. And you can," he added softly, persuasively. "Believe that."

He picked up her clenched hands and gently pried them apart. Long, brown fingers stroked back and forth over the silken skin in a loving caress. "One day, my love, we'll look back on this and laugh. I refuse to believe the love I feel for you could possibly be one-sided. It's too strong, too deep. The problem is that your emotions have been encased in a block of ice for so long they're numb. But the ice cracks a little more every time I touch you. We both know that. With time and patience, it will melt completely, and I think you'll find that you love me too." He stared at her intently, willing her to believe him. "I'm betting my whole future on it, Katy."

Confusion clouded her blue eyes. She felt torn in two directions. Fear still held her in a tight grip, but Trace's words pulled at her heart like a powerful magnet, stirring long-buried dreams. As a child she had woven wonderful fantasies of someday having a marriage like that of her parents, of sharing that kind of deep, boundless love, of having a home of her own and a small brood of beautiful, happy children. That dream had died three years ago. She had buried it so deep that she had not believed it could ever be resurrected. But it had happened. The old yearnings stirred inside her.

Honesty forced Katy to admit that she did feel some sort of basic attraction for Trace. Her body had recognized it long before her conscious mind had accepted the fact. What if he was right, if all he'd said was really possible? Could she love him, wholeheartedly, in every sense of the word?

"Katy, I don't expect an answer now." Trace's voice broke into her thoughts. "But I want your promise that you'll think about it. Will you do that?"

"I—I—" She stopped and chewed worriedly at her lip, her eyes wide and wary. Finally, she took a deep breath and whispered, "Yes. I'll think about it."

"Good. That's all I ask." He patted her hand and stood up. Katy remained in the chair and watched, dazed, as her father saw him to the door. He pushed the screen door part way open, then paused, and turned back to face her. "Just remember, Katy. It's a chance for happiness for both of us. Don't throw it away." Then he was gone.

"Well, my girl, what do you think?" Tom asked as he returned to the sofa.

Agitated, Katy stood up and began to pace the floor in front of the hearth, her heels clicking impatiently against the hardwood floor. She retraced her steps several times, then stopped and flung out her hand, a harried expression on her face. "Oh, I don't know! I *just don't know!*"

"Well, I'll say this. You'll not be gettin' a better proposal than that, me darlin'."

The thickening of his brogue lifted the corners of Katy's mouth. It told her more clearly than words ever could how deeply concerned he was for her.

"I know that, Dad." She folded her arms over her midriff and resumed her pacing. "That is, if he keeps his promises. That was a very pretty speech, I'll admit, but, supposing I did accept, what's to prevent him from claiming his rights after we're married?"

"His word, that's what."

"And you think I can put my trust in that?"

"I know you can. He's a good man, Katy. Believe that."

Shaking fingers raked the silky mass of blue-black hair away from her face, then returned to massage her throbbing temples. "Oh, Dad," she sighed wearily. "How can you be so certain? I keep remembering how wild he used to be. The crazy, impossible things he used to do."

"Aw, Katy, Katy," her father admonished with soft severity. "In those days he was hurtin' badly. The lad was lashin' out at the world in the only way he knew how. Can't you understand that?"

Katy stared at him, transfixed. Less than a week ago Trace had said something very similar about her father. Perhaps the two men were even more alike than she had thought. Was Trace really like her father? Was he one of those strong, rugged men whose masculinity is merely enhanced by his deep capacity for tenderness?

Katy had heard it said that every little girl wanted to marry a man just like her daddy when she grew up. In her own case she knew that was true. She could imagine no finer man in the whole world than Tom Donovan. If Trace was really like him . . . Katy deliberately thrust the thought aside. It was silly, wishful thinking. She had to be practical and level-headed about this.

"Oh, Dad, I just don't know what to do." She sighed in weary confusion.

"Katy, listen to me. Even in his wildest, most hell-raising period, Trace was absolutely trustworthy. When he gave his word, he stood by it, even if it meant taking a thrashing from old Henry."

One corner of her mouth lifted in a rueful smile. "It

sounds as though you think I ought to accept Trace's proposal."

"I'll tell you truly, my girl, if I had the privilege of hand picking a husband for you, I'd choose Trace. He's a good man, Katy. None better. And he loves you deeply. He'll make a fine husband and father, and he'll take good care of you."

"But I don't need a husband to take care of me," she argued.

Tom looked at her sadly, and patted the cushion beside him. "Come here, lass," he ordered, and Katy obeyed. He picked up her hand and squeezed it gently, his tired old eyes warm on her trusting face. "Look at me, darlin'. I'm an old man. I won't be around much longer. I want to know that you have someone, that you won't be alone when I—"

Katy pressed her fingers against his mouth, shutting off the dreadful words. "No! Dad, don't say that!" she cried, but Tom merely shook his head and removed her hand.

"Don't look so stricken, darlin'. Truth to tell, without your mother, I don't much care. You're the only thing that's kept me going this past year." Raising a large, calloused hand, he tucked a lock of hair behind her ear, then trailed his knuckles along the elegant line of her jaw.

"Lookin' at you is like seein' my darlin' Kathleen as she was twenty years ago," he murmured softly. "And you're like her in other ways too. Some women could have shrugged off that attack and gone on with their lives. Some it would even have hardened. But not you, Katy. You're soft and gentle and very vulnerable. You need the love and protection of a good man. I want that for you, Katy, more than anything in this world," he whispered fiercely. "Love, the kind your mother and I had, is life's greatest reward. If you've got that, nothin' else matters."

"But, Dad, I don't love Trace," she protested.

"How do you know that, darlin'? For years you've kept your emotions locked up tight inside you. You haven't let yourself feel anything for any man. Let go, Katy," he urged. "You'll be surprised how good it feels." He gave her hand another squeeze and smiled coaxingly. "And I'll admit, I'd rest easier knowing Trace would be takin' care of you after I've gone."

Tears pushed against her lower lids, then slowly trickled over, leaving wet tracks on the satin-smooth cheeks. As she stared at the lined, weathered face, Katy was forced to accept what her mind had refused to see for the past few years. Her father *was* looking extremely old and tired.

"Oh, Dad." Her voice wavered as she forced out the words. "I suppose, if it means that much to you, and you're sure he can be trusted, I'll marry him. I haven't much choice anyway. If I don't you'll have to give up your job."

Tom reached up and framed her face with his large, work-roughened hands. His brows were drawn together in a concerned frown as he stared into her tear-drenched eyes. "Don't be doin' it for me, Katy darlin'. Do it for yourself. I've known him, man and boy, and I'm tellin' you, you'll not find a better man, or a better husband, than Trace Barnett."

Chapter Six

"You're going to *what!*" Jane squeaked.

"I said I'm going to marry Trace," Katy repeated huskily, keeping her head down, her eyes firmly fixed on the small cup she was washing. She could feel Jane's shocked stare boring into her, but couldn't make herself meet her friend's eyes.

"I *know* what you said. What I want to know is *why?* Less than a week ago you were still avoiding him like the plague, and now you calmly tell me you're going to marry him. Good grief! I'd heard that Trace was a fast worker, but this is ridiculous!" Jane dried another cup with swift, agitated movements and shoved it into the cabinet above the counter. "Oh, I know he put on a good show when he picked you up last Friday, but it was obvious that you were still running scared."

Katy glanced up and smiled wanly. "Trace is rather hard to resist when he wants something badly."

"That I can well imagine!" Jane retorted. "Don't get me wrong. Frank and I were delighted that he was interested in you. It's high time you came out of your shell. But we thought he'd have sense enough to court you slowly and carefully, the way you deserve to be courted. We were even betting that it would be the end of summer before he broke through that wall of reserve. And then probably several months more before things started getting serious between you two. Now this! I tell you, Katy, it looks to me as though you've been bulldozed into something against your will, and I don't like it! Not one bit!"

Katy's hand was trembling as she placed the last dish in the drain rack, and Jane pounced on the betraying reaction like a cat on a mouse.

"Ah-ha! Look at that!" she cried triumphantly, as Katy plunged her hand back into the sudsy water. "Your nerves are as tight as a fiddle string. Don't tell me that's a normal reaction for a radiantly happy bride-to-be, because I'm not buying it."

Jane hung her dish towel on the rack at the end of the counter, then turned to face Katy with her hands planted firmly on her hips. "Now, I want to know what's going on. You're my friend, Katy, and I don't want to see you hurt. And I can tell you, I'm picking up some very peculiar vibrations."

Sighing, Katy dried her hands on a paper towel and turned to meet her friend's demanding stare. She should have known she couldn't fool Jane. Why had she even bothered to try? Jane was very sensitive. She had an instinct about people, especially those to whom she was close. There was nothing else to do but tell her the truth, and that meant starting at the beginning, three years ago. It seemed incredible that the secret she had kept locked inside her for so long was about to be told again, for the second time in the space of just a few days. But, somehow, strangely, it didn't seem to matter anymore.

"All right, Jane. I'll tell you." Katy walked across the room, sank down onto the couch, and motioned for the other woman to join her. "It's rather a long story, so you'd better have a seat."

"Sounds ominous," Jane said, as she curled herself into the opposite corner of the couch. The bristling aggression slowly drained from her as her gaze probed Katy's pale face. Leaning back against the armrest, Jane watched worriedly as Katy struggled to get the words out.

At last she began, slowly and hesitantly, her voice barely more than a whisper, her throat aching. Katy kept her head lowered, her eyes trained on her hands as she began to recite the horrifying story. Several times she had to pause to gather her composure, but she told it all. Forcing the words out in a flat, dull monotone, she described the attack, her father's timely arrival, Henry Barnett's threat, even her own withdrawal into emotional numbness. Then, with the worst behind, her voice grew stronger as she told of Trace's relentless pursuit, her father's desperate action, and, finally, of the incredible proposal.

The air was heavy with emotion when the strained narrative ended, her words vibrating in the deathly silence. The tension was suffocating. Katy's chest was so tight it hurt to breathe. Finally, gathering her courage, she looked up and found that Jane was staring at her with anguished brown eyes, her cheeks wet with unchecked tears.

"Oh, Katy," she choked out, and in the next instant moved across the empty cushion to clasp the younger girl in her arms. "Katy, dearest, why didn't you tell me before? I knew something was wrong, but I never dreamed . . . Oh, God! Katy!"

"I—I just couldn't."

"Mmmm, it took someone as determined as Trace to pry it out of you. And thank God he did!" she declared fervently. "I take back all the things I said about him. My opinion of that man has just gone up like a rocket."

Katy pulled back and looked at her friend. Her eyes were wide with surprise. "Just a few minutes ago you were ranting about this sudden engagement. Now you sound as though you approve."

"Now that I know the whole story, I do. Wholeheartedly!" She smiled and reached up to brush a stray curl away from Katy's face. "Katy, love, if you haven't gotten over the trauma of it in three years, you're not ever going to. Not by yourself, anyway. You need someone gentle and patient to teach you about love, the way it should be. Someone who cares for you deeply. From what you've just told me, I'd say that Trace is that man."

"Thanks for the vote of confidence."

The deep, masculine voice came as a complete surprise to the two women, and both jumped in alarm. Katy whirled around, her eyes widening.

"Trace! What are you doing here?"

"We were going to shop for an engagement ring today. Remember?"

"I thought we were going to do that this evening. After I finish work."

"The stores will be closed by then, love. Or had you forgotten?"

She hadn't. In fact, she had been counting on it. Buying an engagement ring made it seem so official, so final. She had been hoping to delay the purchase for a day or two, to give herself a chance to get used to the idea. From the sardonic amusement in Trace's expression, she was fairly sure he had known exactly what she was up to.

A warm blush started at the base of her throat and surged upward. "Trace, I don't think I'd . . ."

He stepped forward and took hold of her hand, drawing her to her feet in one smooth motion. When she was standing he dropped his arm across her shoulders and smiled down at her. "I doubt very much if your boss would begrudge you an hour or so to shop for your engagement ring." His persuasive gaze switched to the petite woman on the couch. "Would you, Mrs. Cawley?"

"Of course not. And, please, do call me Jane," she replied instantly. "You couldn't have chosen a better time, as a matter of fact. We just put all the little angels down for their afternoon nap. It will be another hour or so before the organized chaos starts again."

"Good. That should give us plenty of time. Thanks, Jane." Trace turned Katy toward the door and urged her forward.

During the ride to the jewelers, Katy sat rigid and silent. Every cell in her body was quivering with tension. This was the first time she had been alone with Trace since accepting his proposal, and the enormity of her decision had suddenly begun to overwhelm her. The rest of her life. She had committed herself to this man *for the rest of her life!*

She slanted him a wary glance from beneath her lashes. Today he was dressed in an impeccable light gray suit, teamed with a dazzling white shirt and a gray and wine striped tie. Evidently he thought the occasion warranted a certain degree of formality. Ruefully, Katy glanced down at her own simple black and white, geometric-patterned sundress with its short, white jacket. She felt positively dowdy by comparison.

As if he were a magnet, her eyes were drawn to him again and again. He looked exceptionally handsome, Katy had to admit. But not even the sophisticated elegance of his attire could conceal the leashed power in that long, lean body or the sheer virility that radiated from him. Just being near Trace made her uneasy. He was so . . . so rawly male.

A shiver rippled through her like an icy wave. What if her father were wrong? What if Trace couldn't be trusted? The dreaded fear began to unfurl itself deep inside her, and Katy felt suddenly cold and clammy. Closing her eyes, she took several deep breaths and forced down the panic that threatened to consume her. No! No, she wouldn't think like that. Her father was a good judge of character, wasn't he. And so far, Trace's behavior had been exemplary.

The night before, when she had told him she would

marry him, his eyes had flared hotly with some dark, intense emotion, but it had been only a fleeting reaction that had faded before she'd had a chance to become frightened. Surprisingly, he had only smiled that slow, heart-stopping smile and said softly, "Thank you, Katy. I promise you won't regret it." Other than giving her one, brief kiss on the cheek, he had made no attempt to touch her.

Determined to live up to her end of the bargain, Katy clamped down on her rising panic. Her resolve wavered slightly when, a short while later, Trace slipped the stunning marquise-cut diamond solitaire on her finger. The unaccustomed weight of the ring and the blatantly possessive look in Trace's eyes brought back some of her doubts. Katy's heart began to beat with a slow thud. Things were moving too fast. For a hysterical moment she actually considered running for the nearest exit.

As though sensing her thoughts, Trace placed his hand under her chin and tipped her face up. She knew her fears were visible in her eyes, but instead of becoming angry or impatient, he sent her a smile of such tender compassion that her heart gave a queer little jerk.

"It's too late for second thoughts, darling. If our jeweler friend hasn't already spread the word, I'm sure the newspaper staff has. You see, I called this morning to have a formal announcement placed in the paper. Besides that, there are several other very good reasons for rushing," he informed her, smiling indulgently into her wary eyes. "Not the least of which, I'll admit, is the fact that I am very anxious to make you my wife. But there's something else, too, something you said the other day that made me realize it would be best if I made my intentions clear."

"Something *I* said?"

"Yes. Katy, I'm well aware of my reputation in this town, especially where women are concerned. I don't want anyone to have any doubts about my feelings for you, or what your position is in my life. For that reason I want this engagement made public as soon as possible."

No matter how hard she tried, Katy could not suppress the warm glow Trace's words had brought. It stayed with her all the way back to the nursery school. It also perplexed her. Why should it please her so much that he obviously cared for her and wanted the whole world to know? It was a difficult question, one that made Katy feel uneasy and somewhat guilty.

Now that she had committed herself and had begun to accept the situation, she realized that their arrangement was actually very one-sided. Trace was being extremely patient and understanding and receiving little in return. In all honesty, she had entered into the bargain with her eyes wide open and really had no cause for complaint. She had given her word and accepted him on his terms, and she might as well make the best of it. It would be pointless not to.

With that decision firmly in mind, she made no protest when Trace accepted Jane's invitation to dinner that night.

They arrived at the Cawleys' front door promptly at eight, to the sound of heavy, discordant rock music issuing from the house at a volume that threatened to shatter the walls. Darting Trace an uncertain glance, Katy reached out to ring the doorbell. The melodious chimes didn't make a dent in the orchestrated bombardment.

Amusement crinkled Trace's eyes. "I think a firmer approach is called for." He practically shouted the words in her ear while reaching around her to pound on the door with the side of his balled fist.

A moment later it was opened, and Frank grimaced apologetically as he motioned them in. Miming for them to follow, he marched into the room where Jason and John lay sprawled on the floor in front of the stereo and turned the volume down.

"Hey! What did you do that for!" they squawked in unison, turning identical, outraged faces toward their father.

"I don't think our guests would care to go deaf before dinner," Frank replied with a complete lack of concern. "If you two think you can manage a vertical position for five minutes I'd like you to meet Katy's fiancé. Trace, these two juvenile delinquents are our sons, Jason and John. Boys, meet Trace Barnett."

"Trace Barnett!" they squeaked together. "You mean the guy who owns Green Meadows Farm?"

"'Fraid so," Trace admitted laconically.

They stared at him for a moment, goggle-eyed, then Jason gave Katy a broad wink and nudged his brother in the ribs. "Boy, I'll say one thing for you, Katy"—he snickered—"when you do something, you do it up brown."

Katy was spared the necessity of answering that because Jane walked into the room, followed closely by Martha.

The Cawleys' eldest was dressed in purple jeans and a pink T-shirt. The lurid message scrawled across her breasts made Katy do a quick double take, then hurriedly turn away, her cheeks a bright pink. She was profoundly glad when the girl sailed right on past them.

"Sorry. Can't stop to chat now," she called over her shoulder, taking the stairs two at a time. "My date will be here any minute."

Jane's mouth twitched. "Revolting, isn't it."

"Absolutely," Katy agreed, rolling her eyes.

Jane laughed, then switched her attention to the man at Katy's side. "Don't panic, Trace. I guarantee it won't be like this all evening."

"That's right." Frank added his assurances. "Tweedledum and Tweedledee here are going to the movies, and Martha is going out with her latest heartthrob."

"Heartthrob! Yuck! That word went out with the biplane," John groaned. He clutched his stomach and staggered toward the door. "I think I'm gonna be sick!"

"Yeah, me too," Jason agreed as he trailed after him. "And the only cure for it is a giant box of popcorn and a root beer."

"That's quite a family you've got," Trace said, laughing, when the door closed behind the two boisterous teenagers. "Is it like this around here all the time?"

"No, not always. Sometimes it's worse." Jane waved her hand toward the sofa. "Why don't we sit down and have a nice, relaxing drink before dinner. I don't know about the rest of you, but believe me, I need one."

Frank had no sooner handed out the drinks and taken a seat than Martha came bounding back down the stairs. "Hi, Katy. Sorry I couldn't stop earlier, but I'm going out with this fabulous new fella, and he gets absolutely furious if I keep him waiting." She quickly eyed Katy's rose silk dress and sighed expressively. "Gee, you look terrific."

"Thanks. You look pretty good yourself." Katy was relieved to see that the jeans and T-shirt had been exchanged for a bright yellow and green sundress with a matching jacket. The petite brown-haired girl was the image of her mother, all pixie charm and bouncing enthusiasm. On her, the brilliantly patterned dress looked perfect.

After introductions were made, Martha, with a directness that rivaled her mother's, studied Katy and Trace intently, her head cocked to one side. For a moment her eyes darted back and forth between them, then she shook her head, as though slightly dazzled by her discovery. "Boy, are you two ever going to make good-looking babies together," she stated with a bluntness that brought instant silence to the room.

Becoming suddenly aware of the four stunned faces staring at her, Martha swept them with a disgusted look. "Well, they will!" she insisted defensively. "It's all in the genes, you know. We learned that in Biology I, for heaven's sake!"

Before anyone could find his tongue, the doorbell rang. Martha let out a squeak and ran to answer it in a flurry of skirts and long, shining hair, her startling observation immediately dismissed from her mind. "That'll be Phillip. See you guys later."

There was a brief, taut silence after the door slammed, then three voices burst out laughing. Katy closed her eyes and turned beet-red.

Her flush deepened when Trace leaned close and whispered, "You see, darling. There's one more reason for us to marry."

"I'm sorry, Katy," Jane sputtered helplessly. "But you know how Martha is. She just says whatever comes into her head."

"Yes. Like someone else I could mention," Frank drawled pointedly.

"Well, subtlety never was my long suit. At least with us Cawley women you always know where we stand." Jane stood up and motioned for Katy to follow. "Come on. We'll give these two a chance to get acquainted while we finish dinner."

The meal went smoothly. Jane had prepared everything in advance so that it could be served with a minimum of fuss—a simple, well-planned menu of green salad, a dish of veal and rice, and broccoli in cheese sauce. For dessert there was a light chocolate-mint pie.

The table conversation was pleasant, sometimes bantering. Trace fit easily into the relaxed atmosphere of the Cawley home, joking and laughing with her friends as though he had known them for years. By the time they retired to the living room for after-dinner coffee, even Katy had relaxed somewhat.

"Tell me, Trace. When is the wedding?" Jane asked interestedly, as she handed him his cup.

The unexpected question brought Katy's head up,

and she found that Trace was studying her thoughtfully. She looked away quickly and took a sip of coffee to cover her nervousness. She hadn't yet adjusted to being engaged. The thought of actually fixing a date paralyzed her with fear.

"We haven't discussed it, but I'm hoping it will be next month," Trace said quietly, his intent gaze fixed on Katy's downbent head.

The long curtain of black hair swung outward in a rippling arc when Katy's head snapped around. "Next month! But that's too soon!" The china cup clattered against its saucer, and Katy bent over to place it on the coffee table. Clasping her hands together tightly to stop their trembling, she turned to Trace with wide, troubled eyes. "We can't get married that quickly, Trace. I—I"—her mind groped for an excuse, any excuse to delay—"Th-there's so much to do before a wedding. I can't possibly be ready in time."

Smiling, Trace ran a finger lightly over the curve of her cheek. "All right, darling. Six weeks. But not one day longer. In three weeks we'll have an engagement party, and three weeks after that we'll be married."

"An engagement party!" All thought of the wedding vanished with the introduction of this new threat. "Oh, do we *have* to? I don't know the first thing about giving a party like that. And . . . and I don't know any of your friends or relatives. I'd make a hopeless mess of the whole thing."

"Don't worry about it, sweetheart. Saundra can handle the party. That's the one thing she's good at," he said with a caustic bite. "Just give her a list of the people you want to invite, and I'll see that she takes care of the rest."

"Speaking of Saundra," Jane drawled in an elaborately casual tone. "How did she take the news of your engagement?"

Mild surprise flickered over Trace's rugged features. "Actually I don't suppose she's heard about it. She went to Dallas to visit friends while I was gone, and she hasn't returned yet."

Probably because, like herself, she hadn't expected him back this soon, Katy thought in a sudden burst of angry cynicism. The mention of Saundra deepened her growing sense of dread. Like a fool, she hadn't given the woman a thought, but there wasn't a doubt in her mind that Saundra would be livid when she heard the news. Suddenly Katy's stomach muscles tightened into a hard knot. She didn't think she could deal with Saundra's vicious anger on top of everything else.

"Will Saundra continue to live at Green Meadows after you and Katy are married?"

"Jane! That's none of your business," Frank ground out warningly. "You have no right to ask questions like that."

Jane tossed her head defiantly and shot her husband a quelling look. "I know that. But Katy has a right to know. After all, it affects her future. But knowing her as well as I do, I'm fairly sure she would never ask. So I'm doing it for her."

"Nevertheless, you shouldn't . . ."

"That's all right, Frank. I don't mind answering Jane's question." Trace looked at her and shrugged, his features screwed up in a rather self-conscious grimace. "Actually, I've never given the matter a thought. Saundra has lived at the farm for so long that it just never occurred to me to ask her to leave. But I wouldn't worry about it too much. She'd always enjoyed being mistress of Green Meadows. Once Katy and I are married and she has to relinquish that position, I doubt she'll stick around very long."

Katy was appalled. Weren't things bad enough without this additional complication? She had no desire to be pitted against Saundra in an open confrontation. Did he really expect her just to walk in and wrest control of the household from that spiteful, vicious woman? Or perhaps he didn't. Perhaps this was all lip service. Her eyes narrowed in sudden suspicion as she studied him through the veil of her lashes. Maybe he didn't believe she could win in a battle of wills with his stepmother. Maybe he didn't want her to win. She couldn't believe he was unaware of Saundra's interest in him. He might not want to marry his father's widow, but he certainly didn't seem averse to having her around.

The progression of her thoughts made Katy's stomach churn, but she was powerless to stop it. That could explain why he was so unconcerned about the physical side of their marriage. No doubt, Saundra would be quite happy to satisfy his male appetites. It was even possible that she was already sharing his bed, if rumor were to be believed.

The rest of the evening passed in a blur. Lost in her own thoughts, Katy sat back and let the conversation flow around her. She was puzzled by the violent emotions that tore at her. Even if her suspicions were correct, why should she care? She didn't love or want Trace. She should feel relieved that he might turn to another woman for physical satisfaction. Shouldn't she?

During the ride home she remained quiet, trying to come to grips with the confused jumble of emotions that plagued her. She had the strangest sensation of being swept along on a tide of events over which she had little or no control. It was very disturbing.

It was only when Trace brought the car to a halt in the drive beside her home that Katy's mind came back to the present. When he switched off the engine and turned to face her, the sudden quiet seemed oppressive and threatening, and she blurted out the first thing that came into her head.

"I'm sorry if Jane's questions embarrassed you."

"I wasn't embarrassed," he said with gentle amusement. "They're very nice people, and they care for you very much. I'm glad of that." His voice deepened to a husky caress. "I want only your happiness, Katy. I happen to love you very much."

She turned to look at him then, her blue eyes wide and searching, probing his face intently. "Do you, Trace?" she asked doubtfully. "Do you really?"

He seemed surprised by her skepticism. His brows rose sharply, and he looked back at her in blank astonishment. "Do you doubt it?"

"Oh, I don't doubt that you *think* you love me." She shrugged one shoulder. "But I can't help but wonder if you're not just reaching out for a fantasy."

Instead of becoming angry, as she had half expected, Trace merely looked at her broodingly for a moment, then smiled. "You're a very perceptive lady," he said softly. "I'm only human, Katy. I have all the same weaknesses and needs as other mortals. I won't try to deny that you epitomize all that I've ever longed for. Not only are you beautiful, and the most exquisitely feminine woman I've ever known, but you've also had the advantage of a loving upbringing by parents who were totally committed to one another and to you. That makes you all the more special, Katy. I want what only you can give me. I need it." His voice hardened to a soft violence that made her skin prickle. "I'm going to have it."

His words did not erase her doubts, but deepened them. Katy stared at him apprehensively. Her fear was reflected in her eyes, and seeing it, Trace frowned.

He paused, as though considering his next words carefully, then asked, "Have you ever wondered just exactly what love is, Katy? Have you ever tried to define it, to put it into words?"

She shook her head mutely, staring at him with wary eyes.

"I've always thought love was finding that one some-one who could fill a need in you that no one else could." His mouth curved in a self-derisive grimace. "Everyone has those needs, those desperate longings, that incomplete feeling. When you find that one person it's like finding your other half, and she fills the emptiness, completes you like the missing piece of a jigsaw puzzle. To me, that's love."

He framed her face between his hands and looked into her eyes, his gaze probing the very depths of her being. "And believe me, Katy, my very soul cries out for you. You're what has been missing from my life, all my life, and I need you very much." The deep, dark velvet voice stroked over her, soothing and caressing, wrapping her in its warmth. "But love isn't altogether selfish. It also means caring more for the happiness and well-being of the loved one than you care for your own. And that's how I feel about you, sweetheart. I could never be happy unless you were."

Katy stared at him, her throat tight with emotion. She felt helplessly drawn by the desperate yearning in his voice, the deep need, the exquisite tenderness. In that moment she knew she was totally, irrevocably committed to this man. Katy knew with a deep certainty that she felt something for him, and that she needed him just as surely as he needed her. She didn't want it. She wasn't ready for it. But it was there all the same. It was that irresistible, magnetic pull she had feared from the beginning. She also knew that if she entered into a marriage with Trace, no matter how platonic, she could never endure the kind of sordid arrangement she had envisioned earlier.

Watching the play of emotions cross her expressive face, Trace smiled gently. He bent and brushed a feathery kiss over her lips. It was possessive and loving, and heart-stoppingly tender. Light as it was, Katy felt it all the way to her toes.

When he raised his head his eyes caressed her face in a way that made her bones melt. "I love you, Katy," he whispered. "Don't ever doubt it."

Chapter Seven

"If you don't hold still, Dad, I'll never get this thing tied," Katy admonished, while her father shifted restlessly from one foot to the other. She thought he looked very handsome and distinguished in his formal evening attire, with his shock of white hair neatly brushed and his deeply tanned skin glowing against the crisp white shirt. But Tom was obviously uncomfortable.

"Humph! I still don't see why I have to get rigged up in this monkey suit," he grumbled, his face like a thunder cloud.

"You have to wear it because this is a formal engagement party. And you may as well get used to wearing it because in the future you'll probably be attending quite a few affairs like this."

Tom's scowl deepened. "The devil you say! I'll be doing no such thing!" he denied vehemently.

"Oh, yes, you will." Katy's voice was calm and placid, as though she were soothing a fractious child. She straightened the loops on the black bow tie and patted it into place, then looked up at her father and smiled. "You were the one who was so anxious for me to marry Trace. Didn't you realize that as his father-in-law you will be expected to attend any social functions we may have in the future?" Eyes twinkling, she reached up and patted his cheek. "Anyway, I know you'll want to come, if for no other reason than to give me moral support—which I shall probably need in large quantity."

Tom's expression altered quickly, concern darkening the gray eyes that searched her face. His hands came up to grasp her shoulders as his brows drew together in an anxious frown. "Katy darlin', you're not marrying Trace for my sake, are you? Because if that's all it is, I won't have it. You're not a sacrificial lamb, my girl. You're my daughter and I want your happiness above all things. I won't deny that I think this marriage is the best thing that could happen to you. But if it isn't going to make you happy, I'll admit to being an interfering old fool and go see Trace right now and call the whole thing off."

The smile faded from Katy's face and her eyes grew distant as she chewed worriedly on her bottom lip. It was a temptation. Her father could go to him and put a stop to the arrangement immediately. Then she could return to the safe, calm life she had led before his return. Couldn't she?

But even as she asked herself the question Katy knew deep down inside that it simply wasn't that easy. She was bound to Trace now in some strange, indefinable way that had nothing to do with concern for her father or even a longing for security. Her mind shied away from examining her feelings too closely, but she knew that her future lay with Trace. It was as though on that day at the graveside, almost two months ago, when she had looked up and met his eyes, the thread of her life had become inextricably woven with his.

"Answer me, Katy. Why did you agree to this marriage?"

Her father's concerned voice brought her out of her

thoughts. She shook her head and gave him a wan smile. "I—I honestly don't know. At first I told myself I was doing it for you, so that your future would be secure, and because it would make you happy. But now, I'm not sure. I'm just . . . not sure."

Tom lifted one hand and cupped her cheek. A gentle smile replaced the tense anxiety in his face. "Don't worry about it, darlin'. Just follow your instincts. You won't go wrong."

He kissed her on the forehead, then turned her around and gave her a little push. "Now then, go get your things, girl, and let's be going. Trace wanted us there half an hour ago. He's going to think you got cold feet at the last minute."

In her room Katy deliberately took her time, unnecessarily recombing her hair and checking her appearance for perhaps the tenth time. She had no intention of arriving at the big house any earlier than she absolutely had to. The less she had to endure of Saundra's company the better.

The woman was impossible! On the surface, at least in front of Trace, she had been the soul of politeness and congeniality, seeming to accept the engagement with good grace, if not enthusiasm. But whenever Trace was not around Saundra's tongue dripped pure poison. She needled Katy constantly with malicious little remarks about her lack of sophistication and her modest family background, hinting that she was only kidding herself if she actually believed the marriage would take place. Saundra seemed confident that Trace would call the whole thing off before the wedding day arrived. Since that was only three weeks away, it seemed unlikely, but still, the malicious little innuendos were getting under Katy's skin.

Katy had not mentioned the matter to Trace. She had wanted to, several times, but whenever she worked up the courage to discuss the situation she was suddenly besieged with tormenting doubts and questions. What if they really were having an affair, as Saundra had implied on several occasions? What if he had no intention of cutting his stepmother out of his life after they were married? As far as she knew, during the three weeks since they had become engaged, he had done nothing toward persuading Saundra to move out of the house. And the woman certainly acted as though she were a permanent fixture.

It was a situation that could not be allowed to continue. Sometime between now and the wedding Katy knew she was going to have to talk to Trace and settle the matter, once and for all. She could not . . . she *would* not share either a husband or a house with Saundra Barnett!

When they pulled up in front of the big house Trace was waiting for them, nervously pacing the front veranda like a caged lion. Before Katy could locate the handle and open the door, he was beside the truck.

"What took you so long, darling?" he asked anxiously, as he helped her out. "I was beginning to get concerned."

Katy opened her mouth to answer but the words stuck in her throat when she saw the uncertainty in Trace's eyes. He looked terribly worried. Frightened almost. For the first time she realized that he was very vulnerable where she was concerned, and the knowledge made her heart contract with a strangely pleasurable pain. Did he really love her? Until now she hadn't put much stock in his avowal, but his attitude seemed to confirm it. It was a heady thought, and for a moment she could only stare at him, her pulse throbbing wildly in her throat.

The lines of strain slowly eased from Trace's face as he drank in the sight of her. A small flame leaped in the hazel depths when his eyes met hers and clung.

"Well, my boy, I'm sorry we're so late," Tom said,

breaking into the strange spell that locked them together. "But you know how it is when women get to primping. I hope none of the guests have arrived yet."

"No, not yet. But they should start arriving any time now." Holding both of Katy's hands, Trace stepped back and let his warm gaze roam over her from head to toe, then back again. "And I must say, your daughter is well worth waiting for."

A warm blush flooded Katy's cheeks when she met that intent, possessive stare. Blatant, male appreciation written in every line of his ruggedly handsome face, Trace repeated his inspection, slower this time.

Her chiffon dress was a pale powder blue at the top, where the simple draped bodice, supported by two thin straps, lovingly clung to her breasts and waist. From there the flared, floating skirt gradually deepened in color, reaching a dark midnight blue where it swirled like a delicate cloud around her ankles. It was an utterly simple, devastatingly feminine dress that gave her skin a pearly cast and brought out the color of her eyes.

It was part of the new wardrobe Trace had insisted upon buying for her. It seemed to Katy that she had bought more clothes in the past three weeks than she had in her entire adult life. With Jane's help, she had scoured all of the Tyler dress shops and a good many in Dallas as well. She had been hesitant about accepting his offer, but now, seeing the look in his eyes, Katy was glad she had. In any case, she knew that, as mistress of Green Meadows, she would need presentable clothes, and her father certainly couldn't afford to pay for such an elegant trousseau.

Smiling, Trace placed his hand lightly on the back of her waist and urged her toward the house. "Come inside. If we hurry, I'll just have time to give you your engagement present before our guests start arriving."

"Another present? Trace, you shouldn't have done that. You've given me so much already."

Her protests fell on deaf ears. Inside the house, Trace ushered her into his study and closed the door behind them. While she stood uncertainly in the middle of the floor he went to his desk, unlocked it and removed a square, flat box from the top drawer.

"I hope you like it," he said softly, as he placed it in her trembling hands. "When I saw it, I thought of you."

Katy lifted the lid and gasped. "Oh, Trace. It's beautiful."

In the velvet-lined box lay a necklace of brilliant sapphires and diamonds. In the finely wrought setting they resembled a chain of exquisite flowers, each vivid blue stone surrounded by a circle of diamonds and nestled in a bed of platinum leaves. The clusters were connected by an entwined strand that resembled a delicate, trailing vine.

"Here, let me put it on for you," he offered, as she continued to gape at the sparkling necklace.

Katy obediently turned around, and as the cool stones settled against her skin, she tilted her head forward and pulled the long fall of hair over her shoulder, exposing the nape of her neck. The feel of his warm fingers brushing against her flesh made Katy shiver.

Trace guided her to the wall mirror and stood behind her, his hands on her shoulders. His eyes met hers in the mirror. "Do you like it, Katy?"

"Oh, Trace. How could anyone not like it? It's the most beautiful thing I've ever seen."

"Does it deserve a kiss?"

She stared at his reflection, her heart pounding against her chest. During the past three weeks he had made no attempt to kiss her, other than brushing his lips across her forehead when he told her good night. He had touched her often, his hand cupping her elbow, or lightly pressing against the small of her back when they walked together, or sometimes just holding hers, but never in any way that frightened her or made her unduly nervous. But now he wanted to kiss her. Though she didn't find the idea totally repugnant, Katy wasn't sure she wanted their current, easy relationship to change.

Seeing the indecision in her eyes, Trace took it for refusal. "Forget it, Katy," he said with soft regret. "I didn't mean to press you."

Strangely, his quick retraction made up her mind for her, and, turning around, she placed her hand on his arm. "No, Trace, I—I didn't . . . I mean . . . if you want to kiss me, you may," she offered hesitantly.

"Are you sure?"

She wasn't. She wasn't sure at all. But it was too late to back out now. Swallowing her fear, she nodded.

Very gently, very cautiously, Trace slipped an arm around her waist and drew her close. His other hand came up under her chin and cupped her jaw, tilting her head up. An incredibly tender light glittered in the deep-set hazel eyes as they roamed over her face, touching on each delicate feature like a caress.

Trembling within that gentle, possessive embrace, Katy was acutely aware of the warmth of his body against hers, that clean, masculine scent she had come to associate with Trace alone, and the heavy throb of his heart beneath her hand. Her own heart was racing so fast she thought for a moment she was going to faint. But then, as his head began a slow, purposeful descent, Trace whispered, "I love you, Katy," and her eyes fluttered shut.

The kiss was soft, and infinitely gentle. His lips caressed hers with a tender passion that was rigidly controlled, tasting and exploring their trembling softness almost reverently. Katy was shaking, but she knew it was not altogether from fear. An almost unbearable excitement tingled through her like an electric current.

Trace made no effort to deepen the kiss and, after a

moment, drew slowly away and smiled down into her face.

"Did you find that too unbearable?" he asked huskily.

"No." The surprise in her voice was plain, even to her own ears, and Trace's smile widened.

"Good. That's an encouraging sign."

Frowning, Katy opened her mouth to speak, but at that moment there was a sharp rap on the door, then it was thrust open and Saundra stepped inside.

Her expression grew hard when she spied the embracing couple. It grew even harder when her eyes lit on the necklace encircling Katy's throat. "For heaven's sake, Trace! This is hardly the time for kiss and cuddle," she snapped, and Katy felt her face crimson. "The first carload of guests has just driven up. I hope you don't expect me to entertain them alone."

The next half hour was spent greeting the steady stream of guests. Katy stood at Trace's side, a stiff, polite smile pasted on her face as she was introduced to one stranger after another. It wasn't long until the house was overflowing.

It seemed that all of Trace's relatives, no matter how distant, had come to take a look at the woman he had chosen. Katy squirmed under their intent scrutiny. Her stomach was fluttering with nerves. In addition to his family, he had also invited all his friends and business acquaintances. The only people Katy knew were Jane and Frank, and the other farm workers and their families.

Saundra had been livid over the inclusion of the workers, but Katy had very quietly and firmly insisted that they be invited, and in the end she had won. She and her father had no relatives in the United States. Except for the Cawleys, the other workers and their families were her only friends, and she was determined that they should attend the party. All Saundra's pro-

tests had fallen on deaf ears, and her appeal to Trace
had met with equal failure. He had backed Katy to the
hilt.

During the entire evening Trace remained close to
Katy's side, his arm curved possessively around her
waist, or draped over her shoulders as they circulated
among the guests. Katy met so many new people that
she was positive she would never keep the names
straight and after a while even stopped trying. She was
acutely aware of the many covert glances they received
and could not help but wonder if they looked like a
happily engaged couple. Trace certainly appeared
happy, but Katy was very much afraid her own apprehension was plain for everyone to see.

The formal announcement of their engagement was
made around ten o'clock. Katy suffered deep embarrassment at being the cynosure of every pair of eyes in
the room, but at least when it was over she felt that the
worst was behind her, and her nervous tension began to
ease somewhat.

After the toasts were made and the good wishes were
received, Trace maneuvered them through the crowd to
join the Cawleys and Katy's father, standing a little to
one side by the open French doors that led onto the
patio.

"Katy, dearest, you look absolutely gorgeous tonight," Jane said, smiling up at her when they joined
the group. "And I must say, you've handled this whole
affair quite well. Before you know it, parties like this
will be old hat to you."

"Not if I have anything to say about it," Trace
interjected. "We'll entertain occasionally, a few close
relatives and friends, but nothing on the scale of the
parties that my father and Saundra gave. I prefer a
more quiet life, and I think Katy does also." He waved
his hand in an encompassing gesture. "This party
tonight is a once-in-a-lifetime occasion."

Katy sent him a grateful smile. "I'm so glad to hear

you say that. I don't think I could endure this sort of thing too often."

"Don't worry, sweetheart, you won't have to. I've no intention of getting caught up in a mad social whirl. That was part of my quarrel with my father, one of the reasons why I left the farm four years ago. Our priorities didn't mesh at all. His idea of what was important and mine were diametrically opposed."

Katy looked up at him, surprised. This was the first time he had mentioned the quarrel with his father. Though she didn't want to believe it, she couldn't help but wonder if his other reason for leaving had to do with Saundra.

"I echo my daughter's thanks, Trace," Tom said in a relieved tone. "She informed me tonight I'd have to attend whatever parties you two hosted, and I'll confess I wasn't looking forward to becoming a social butterfly at this late stage in life."

Trace laughed aloud at the look of outright distaste on the older man's face. "We'll make it as easy on you as we can, Tom."

Katy felt as though a load had been lifted from her shoulders. Smiling, she turned her head to speak to Jane and froze, the words dying on her lips as she caught sight of Saundra making her way toward them, her arms linked familiarly with the two men on either side of her. Shock widened Katy's eyes and drained every hint of color from her face. Her features working convulsively, she began to shake her head from side to side, a stark, mindless terror gripping her.

The violent tremors shaking her body were transmitted to Trace through his encircling arm, and he looked down at her quickly, alarm leaping into his eyes at her tormented expression.

"My God! What is it, Katy? What's wrong?" he demanded in a frantic voice.

But Katy was incapable of speech. Looking at her panic-stricken face, Trace realized she hadn't even heard him. Fear had her by the throat; she was oblivious to everything else. When she tried to back away Trace wouldn't let her, his arms tightening protectively around her as his eyes made an urgent, sweeping search of the room, seeking the cause of her distress.

It was then he noticed Tom's aggressive stance. His huge frame was taut and poised menacingly. His hands were bunched into tight fists at his sides. A low, vicious growl rumbled from the older man's chest. He was like a wild animal tensing for attack.

Trace tracked Tom's murderous gaze to the approaching trio, then swung back sharply, his eyes narrowing in dawning comprehension. His face grew hard, his body stiffening as he unconsciously drew Katy nearer.

"They're the ones, aren't they?" he asked in a dangerously soft voice.

Both Jane and Frank looked at him in wary confusion, sensing the deadly threat in his tone and wondering at the cause. Wisely, both remained silent.

"Yes." Tom spat the word out. His rage was almost a tangible thing.

"Trace, darling. Look who's here," Saundra called, her eyes sparkling with malicious glee.

Paralyzed with fear, Katy stared at the two men, bile rising in her throat as she met their nasty, knowing smiles. Never, *never* would she forget those faces. At the moment they wore the haughty, bored look common among the idle rich in Saundra's social circle, but Katy could still see the vicious anger that had twisted those aristocratic features three years ago, the terrible, ugly violence that had flared out of control. Tearing her eyes away, she tried to force back the ghastly, terrifying memories, but it was no use. She could feel their eyes on her, and her skin crawled.

There was no remorse in them, no apology, no guilt. They didn't even bother to hide their amusement, their vindictive, slightly lustful eyes sliding insultingly over her.

"This is Vince Wilby and Edgar Hollis. Two very dear, *very* close friends of Katy's," Saundra continued in an insinuating voice. Her smile grew wider when her attention switched to the ashen-faced girl in Trace's arms, her brows arching in feigned surprise. "Why, whatever is the matter, Katy? Don't tell me you're shy? Surely not! Not after the . . . ah . . . intimate relationship you shared with Vince and Edgar a few years ago?"

The poisonous innuendo tore an anguished cry from Katy's throat. Turning blindly, she buried her face against Trace's chest.

His hand came up to cradle the back of her head and press her closer as he strained to absorb the convulsive shudders that racked her slender frame. Burning anger radiated from him in white-hot waves.

"Did you invite these men here?" His eyes stabbed through Saundra with the deadly precision of cold steel.

Saundra could not ignore the barely leashed fury in his tone, or the protective way he held the frightened girl in his arms. Her carefully made-up face grew hard, her eyes glittering with hatred. All pretense of friendliness was dropped.

"Yes!" she flared defiantly. "Did you really think I'd just stand by calmly and watch you make a fool of yourself by marrying this . . . this *nobody?* She's nothing but a cheap tramp. Just ask Vince and Edgar. They can tell you. . . ."

"Shut up, Saundra," Trace snarled.

"No! I won't shut up! Did you know that your precious fiancée is nothing but a tawdry little tease? That only a few years ago she deliberately lured poor Vince and Edgar here into the woods and—"

"*That's enough!*" Trace's hard-boned face was white with anger, his nostrils pinched, his mouth a hard line.

A muscle twitching in his cheek warned of his tenuous control over the rage building within him. "I have never hit a woman in my life," he grated through clenched teeth. "But I swear to you, Saundra, you say one more word against Katy and I'll slap you silly."

Saundra blanched and stepped back. It was no bluff, and she knew it.

The two men at her side stirred restlessly, their eyes shifting with uncertainty between Saundra and Trace. The leering grins had disappeared.

Very slowly, with dangerous deliberation, Trace turned to Jane and handed Katy into her care. "Take her to the study and give her some brandy, will you? I'll be there just as soon as I've cleared out the vermin."

He turned his cold, implacable gaze on Saundra. "You've got exactly thirty minutes to pack your bags and get out. If you're not gone by then, I'll throw you out bodily, with a great deal of pleasure."

"You can't do this to me!" she protested angrily. "This is my home!"

"Correction. This is *my* home. And you're no longer welcome here."

Saundra sputtered and fumed for a moment, but Trace's hard, unblinking stare finally silenced her. With one last, furious glare in Katy's direction, she spun on her heel and stalked out.

Vince and Edgar turned to follow, but Trace stopped them. His voice was ominously soft, an unmistakable, steely threat running through the velvet tones.

"Oh, no. I think not. We have some unfinished business, I believe." He bared his teeth in a travesty of a smile as he met their startled glances. There was no doubt of his intent.

"Now see here," the man called Vince began to bluster. His eyes darted nervously to his companion for support. "If you think we're going to stand still for this . . ."

"I don't think. I know." Trace's voice cut across his protest like a well-honed axe. The finality in his tone was chilling.

Stepping to one side, he gestured toward the patio doors. "Shall we step outside. Unless, of course, you'd like me to wipe up the floor with you right here in front of the other guests."

The two men turned a sickly gray, perspiration beading their faces. Edgar Hollis swallowed hard and ran one finger around the inside of his collar. "Come now, Mr. Barnett, can't we talk this over? There's no need for violence."

"Oh, there's a need, all right," Trace assured him, softly, dangerously. "I feel a fierce need."

Shrugging out of his jacket, he handed it to Frank, his eyes never leaving the two cowering men. With slow, deliberate movements, he began to roll up his shirt sleeves. "Now, you two can either walk out that door in the next five seconds, or I'll haul you both out by the scruff of the neck. The choice is yours."

"Do you need any help?" Frank asked as the two men moved reluctantly toward the door. Having heard the story from his wife, Frank had worked out the reason for Trace and Tom's anger, and his own slow-rising temper had flared hotly.

"Thanks, but no. This privilege belongs solely to Tom and me." Trace smiled and looked at his future father-in-law, his eyes glowing with anticipation. "I think we can handle this. Don't you, Tom?"

Tom brightened instantly. He rubbed his hands together, a slow, eager smile splitting his face. "You know it, lad. You know it."

Katy could barely recall being led through the crowd of interested spectators, or drinking the glass of brandy Frank had pressed into her hand. Reaction had set in. She lay curled in a tight ball on the leather sofa in

Trace's study, her fist jammed against her mouth. Her eyes were strangely blank and her skin looked like alabaster. She made no sound. No move.

Jane sat beside her on the couch and stroked the silky black hair away from Katy's temple. Her eyes were clouded with worry. Now and then her gaze sought her husband, as he paced restlessly up and down the room, but neither said a word.

Finally, after what seemed like an eternity, the door was thrust open and Trace entered. His eyes went immediately to the huddled figure on the couch. In three long strides he crossed the room and knelt beside her. There was a slight tremor in the hand that gently cupped her face.

"Are you all right, darling?" he asked with soft urgency. His gaze roamed restlessly over her face, worry and concern tightening his rugged features.

His words seemed to break through the trance that held her. Katy turned her head slowly and gave him an anguished look. Her chin quivering, she closed her eyes against the threatening tears and nodded.

In the next instant Trace stood up and gathered her into his arms, then sank back onto the couch and settled her on his lap, hugging her close. Neither noticed when Jane and Frank slipped discreetly out the door and closed it behind them.

Trace rocked Katy back and forth, his hands roaming soothingly over her body as he pressed soft kisses over her face. Katy, feeling truly safe at last, burrowed deeper into the security of his warm embrace.

"Oh, Katy," Trace breathed raggedly against her temple. "I'm so sorry, sweetheart. If I had only known what she was up to, I would have put a stop to it. But I can promise you, nothing like that will *ever* happen again. Saundra is gone from our lives for good, and after tonight her two friends won't dare show their faces around here again."

Something in his tone sent a shaft of fear through

her, and Katy grew still. Slowly, she pulled back and searched his face with wide, apprehensive eyes. For the first time, she noticed his hair was disarrayed, and there was a tiny cut at the corner of his mouth. When he lifted his hand to stroke the side of her face she saw that his knuckles were scraped and bleeding, and her stomach clenched sickeningly.

"What did you do to them, Trace?" she whispered.

He grinned. "Your father and I gave them just a small portion of the punishment they deserved," he said with hard satisfaction.

"My father? You let my *father* fight them? Trace! How *could* you? He's an old man. He could have been seriously hurt!"

Trace laughed heartily. "Katy, love, Tom may be sixty-three, but he's as strong as a bull." His eyes twinkled at her. "I'm just glad he was on my side."

Katy stared at him, appalled. There was an aura of suppressed excitement about him, a triumphant joy at having beaten two men senseless, and she found it terrifying. Were all men the same? Did they all find violence exciting? The thought sent a cold trickle down her spine.

"You enjoyed it, didn't you?" she burst out agitatedly, unable to hide the bitter accusation in her voice. "You enjoyed it, and that makes you no better than those two men."

"Katy!" Trace looked as though she had slapped him. He stared at her with disbelieving eyes. "Katy, you're not frightened of me, are you?" he asked finally, and groaned when she nodded. He closed his eyes for a second, a look of intense pain flickering across his face. "Oh, Katy," he whispered sadly. "Don't you know I'd never hurt you? *Never!* You have to believe that, darling. You have to."

Katy's heart thumped with a slow, heavy beat. She looked at him uncertainly. Did she dare trust him? She had always been frightened by his raw masculinity, his overwhelming virility, but this new threat was even worse. What if he became angry or frustrated when their marriage remained platonic, as she fully intended it would? Would he turn violent? Did she dare risk that? The wedding was only three weeks away. If she was going to back out, she had to do it soon. Yet, how could she?

As though reading her mind, Trace pulled her close. "Don't walk away from me, Katy," he whispered urgently, burying his face in the cloud of hair at her neck. "Give me a chance to make you happy. To make us both happy. Trust me, darling. Please."

Katy remained rigid in his arms for a few seconds. Then, slowly, she relaxed against him, and rested her head on his shoulder.

Chapter Eight

Katy looked beyond the airplane's wing to the faint, rosy glow on the horizon, where the ocean met the sky. They had been chasing the sun for hours, but it had steadily outdistanced them, and the fiery ball had sunk majestically into the blue Pacific only moments before. Pulling her eyes away from the gathering dusk of early evening, Katy sighed.

As though drawn by a magnet, her gaze lowered to the rings on her left hand. She touched a finger to them gently, almost fearfully. Well, she had done it. That morning, on her father's arm, wearing her mother's creamy white wedding dress and her grandmother's veil, she had walked down the church aisle and joined her life, irrevocably, to Trace's. She was committed now. There could be no turning back.

Of the ceremony she remembered very little. The sea of faces watching her had not registered, nor had the profusion of flowers in the church, nor the stirring chords of the wedding march that had thundered from the organ. The only thing she had been aware of was the tall, incredibly handsome man waiting for her at the end of the aisle, watching her approach with an intensity that made her already shaking knees go weak as water. If it hadn't been for her father's support, she would have crumpled to the floor in a little heap of satin and lace and quivering flesh. From the moment she stepped into the church, Trace's eyes had seemed to pierce right through the misty cloud of tulle that billowed around her head and shoulders, his expression so warm and tender, so blatantly, proudly possessive that her heart had leaped up into her throat and stuck there.

Katy supposed she must have spoken her wedding vows, though she couldn't recall doing so. When Trace had taken her icy, trembling hand in his, her mind had gone blank. It wasn't until he lifted the veil over her head and kissed her softly on the lips that she had come out of her daze.

The reception afterwards had been an ordeal, and she had been profoundly grateful when Trace had suggested that they leave.

Katy sighed and returned her gaze to the window. Now, here they were on their way to Hawaii to begin a honeymoon that wasn't to be a honeymoon at all. She hoped.

There was a soft ping, then the stewardess's voice was informing them that they were beginning their descent into the Honolulu airport and asking everyone to please buckle their seatbelts. Immediately Katy stiffened.

She had never flown before. Earlier, during the short flight from Tyler to Dallas, she had been pale and shaken. But when the jumbo jet had roared down the Dallas runway and strained into the sky, she had been petrified.

Katy felt the plane slip downward and closed her eyes tightly, then jumped as Trace's warm hand covered hers.

"Relax, darling," he whispered. Smiling, he gently pried her white-knuckled fingers from the armrest. Still holding her hand, he slipped his other arm around her and pulled her close. "Just shut your eyes and lean on me. We'll be down before you know it."

Katy complied gratefully, feeling ridiculously secure with his arm wrapped around her, her face pressed against the fine material of his dark, three-piece suit.

After receiving the traditional Hawaiian greeting, Trace guided them through the hustle and bustle of the airport with a minimum of fuss. Within minutes, Katy was sitting in a taxi, fingering the lei of white ginger blossoms that encircled her neck.

The hotel Trace had chosen for them was one of the most plush on Waikiki Beach. When they entered the lobby, Katy was pleased to see that it was moderately full. Somehow she felt safer with other people around. Which was why, when Trace left the choice up to her, she had elected to come to Hawaii for their honeymoon. It was beautiful and exciting, but more important, it was packed with people. She didn't want to be alone in some isolated, romantic spot with Trace.

Katy stood nervously by and watched as he signed the register, a satisfied smile curving his mouth as he wrote "Mr. and Mrs. Trace Barnett" in a clear, bold hand. By the time they entered their ninth floor suite her stomach felt as though it contained a thousand butterflies.

The suite was elegant and beautiful, but Katy was too keyed up to notice. She was acutely aware that this night would prove whether her father's trust in Trace was justified, and with every second that ticked by, her doubts grew, stretching her nerves to breaking point.

What if he had been wrong? What if? . . .

When Trace and the bellboy disappeared into the adjoining room, Katy stumbled to the balcony doors and tugged them open. Her breath was coming in short gasps as she crossed to the waist-high railing and clutched it desperately. A soft breeze gently lifted the heavy tumble of hair off her shoulders. The moon painted the midnight-blue ocean with streaks of silver, illuminating the frothy, lace-edged waves as they slid onto the sand far below.

Katy stared blindly at the romantic scene. God! She'd been a fool to enter into this crazy arrangement! What did she really know about Trace, other than that he wanted her and seemed willing to go to any lengths to get her? Even her father didn't really know him. After all, Trace had been gone for four years, and people could change a lot in that time. No! No, she wouldn't think that way. She couldn't! She'd go mad if she did.

Taking long, deep breaths, Katy forced herself to remember how tender Trace had been with her, how considerate, how concerned. Yet on the heels of that thought she recalled how violent he could be when angered, his fury a cold, frightening menace. So far he had only shown her his gentle side, but she knew there was another. She had glimpsed it the night of their engagement party.

"So this is where you disappeared to. You had me worried there for a minute."

Katy flinched at the sound of Trace's voice, just behind her, then flinched again when his hands closed warmly around the curves of her shoulders. She held her breath and fought to control her trembling body. Her knuckles were white as she gripped the railing. The slow movement of his hand, though meant to be soothing, did little to help.

"There's nothing to be frightened of, Katy," he murmured softly as he felt her reaction. "You must believe that."

Unable to speak, Katy swallowed hard and nodded. She felt brittle, ready to shatter.

There was a moment of tense silence, then Trace continued in a deliberately lighter tone. "You hardly touched your meal on the plane. Would you like to go downstairs for dinner?"

"No, thank you. I'm really not hungry."

"Well, in that case, why don't you go in and get ready for bed. I know it's fairly early here, but our bodies are still on Texas time. I suggest that we get a good night's rest, so we'll be in shape to start our tour of the islands in the morning."

Katy turned slowly to search his face, and met only tenderness and understanding in the hazel eyes. Her heartbeat began to slow to normal. "I—I think I will," she stammered weakly. "I'm very tired. It's been a long day."

Smiling, Trace put his arm around her shoulders and led her inside, releasing her as they reached the bedroom. Katy gave him a wan smile and stepped through the door, only to come to a skidding halt just inside, color draining from her face at the sight of the huge, king-sized bed that dominated the room.

There was a loud roaring in her ears as the blood began to pound through her veins. Dizzy with fear and rage, she whirled around to find Trace's large frame filling the doorway. He was very still, watching her intently.

"You lied to me!" she screamed, backing away. "You've been lying from the very beginning."

"I didn't lie. You've known all along that I meant for us to share a bedroom."

"A bedroom, yes! But not the same bed!"

"Yes, Katy, the same bed. Both here and at home."

Panic clawed at her. She took another step backward, her head moving slowly from side to side, her face distraught. Her heart was beating so hard she was almost suffocating. "No! No, I won't do it! I won't let you do this to me! You promised you wouldn't. . . ."

"Stop it!" Trace covered the distance between them and grasped her by the shoulders, shaking her gently. "Stop it, right now. You're becoming hysterical. I have no intention of breaking my word to you. I'm not going to make love to you, Katy, until you ask me to. But I *am* going to hold my wife in my arms when I go to bed at night." He pulled her close and wrapped her in an unyielding embrace, holding her terrified eyes with an intent, unwavering look. "Oh, darling. Don't you see? If our marriage is ever to have a chance we've got to get you accustomed to being close to me, to touching and being touched. It's normal and natural." He stopped and gave her a teasing smile, lifting one hand to trail his knuckles down the line of her jaw. "And once you get used to it, I think you'll find it quite enjoyable."

Katy swallowed hard. Her heart was still banging away at her ribcage. "Th-that's all? You won't . . ."

"No. I'd never take advantage of you," he assured her quickly. He stared at her, willing her to believe him. The sincerity in his expression was unmistakable. "I don't just want your body, my darling. I'm greedy. I want your love, and I want you to give it to me freely."

He released her and turned her toward the adjoining bath. "Now, get ready for bed, woman. We have a busy day ahead tomorrow."

Katy stumbled into the bathroom on rubbery legs. She showered, slipped into her nightgown, brushed her teeth and hair and creamed her face, all in a frozen daze. The thought of spending the night in Trace's arms made her feel faint. How could she possibly do it? Yet, what choice did she have? She had accepted his terms six weeks ago, and so far he had lived up to his side of the bargain scrupulously. She could hardly do less.

Katy slid the white silk and ecru lace negligee over her matching gown and tied the bow just under her breasts. Then, her throat dry, she reached for the doorknob.

Only a dim pool of light from the bedside lamp lit the room, but it was enough for her to see that Trace was already in bed. His muscular chest was bare, and in the soft light, the curling mat of hair that covered it gleamed like burnished gold. Against the white sheets his skin was a deep bronze, his shoulders unbelievably broad. Katy's heart took off like a jackhammer. She stood rooted to the spot.

A slow smile curved Trace's mouth as he turned back the covers and held out his hand invitingly. "Come to bed, my darling," he whispered.

As though pulled by an invisible string, Katy walked slowly toward him, unable to look away from that intent, hazel stare. Trembling violently and flushing a deep crimson at the appreciative gleam in his eyes, she took off the thin negligee and dropped it across the end of the bed, then slid in beside him. At once Trace's arms closed around her.

Her body stiffened as she felt herself drawn against his hard length, but when she tried to strain away his arms tightened.

"No, don't tense up like that, sweetheart. Just relax and put your head on my shoulder." The encircling arm held her close, his hand cupping her hipbone and rubbing it rhythmically, while the other gently, but firmly, curved around the side of her head and pushed it down until she felt the warmth of his skin beneath her cheek.

Katy could scarcely breathe. The incredible intimacy had every nerve in her body wound to violin-string tautness. The warmth of his flesh seared her from forehead to toes. The musky, masculine scent of him was all around her, invading her body with every shallow breath she drew, making her giddy. She felt warm and protected, and cold and afraid, all at the same time.

The lamp clicked off and the room was flooded with darkness. Trace's breath stirred the hair at her temple as he placed a soft kiss on her forehead. "Good night, darling. Sleep well," he murmured.

She almost giggled hysterically. Sleep well? *Sleep well?* How on *earth* could she sleep when she felt as though she were about to explode into a million little pieces?

Long after the caressing hand at her hip had ceased its motion, Katy lay rigid at Trace's side, staring into the darkness, listening to the slow, strong thud of his heart beneath her ear, feeling the steady rise and fall of his massive chest. How could he sleep? She certainly couldn't. But then, Trace was probably used to sleeping with a woman in his arms. The thought was painful, and Katy's mind immediately shied away from it.

For what seemed like hours, she lay perfectly still, not daring to even blink. But finally, little by little, her taut muscles began to go slack, and her lashes fluttered downward, brushing against the bronzed shoulder that cradled her head. The small, tight fist which lay across the masculine chest slowly uncurled. Smiling, Trace covered the delicate hand with his own larger one, and pressed it tightly to him.

When she opened her eyes, the room was filled with sunshine, and Trace, propped up on one elbow, was smiling down at her.

"Good morning, wife," he greeted cheerfully, then laughed aloud as a tide of deep color rose from her neck all the way to her hairline.

Flustered by his nearness, and acutely aware of her vulnerable position, Katy's eyes darted around in a frantic effort to avoid the muscular chest, just inches from her nose. It was an impossible task. Finally she gave up and focused intently on the hollow at the base of his throat.

"Good—good morning."

Her stammered reply brought another chuckle from Trace. Then he reached out a hand and brushed the tousled strands of hair away from her face. "Do you know you're even more beautiful when you're asleep? You look so soft and cuddly with your face scrubbed and clean, and all that glorious hair spread out on the pillow." The words seemed to be drawn out of him slowly, a low husky passion roughening his voice.

Katy lay mesmerized, unable to look away from that hard, sensuous mouth as it drew inexorably nearer. Warm breath feathered against her skin as he added softly, "I don't know how I managed to wait this long for my good morning kiss."

Then his mouth found its target. The kiss was exquisite, his lips moving over hers with great tenderness, coaxing, imploring, enticing. The tip of his tongue traced back and forth between her slightly parted lips, only just penetrating into the sweet moistness within, yet the tiny invasion was excruciatingly sensual and explosive. Its shock waves rocked Katy to her toes. Her soft mouth quivered beneath his as fear and intense pleasure battled for control.

Meeting no resistance, Trace leaned closer. His bare chest brushed the tips of her breasts through their thin covering as one hand closed possessively around the inverted curve of her waist. For an instant Katy's trembling fingers hovered just a scant inch from his chest. Then, drawn by a power beyond her control, they settled against the hard, muscled flesh and threaded hesitantly through the crisp hair that covered it.

Trace's instant response was a shuddering moan. The hand at her waist stirred as the pressure of his mouth increased.

Katy felt like a tightly wound spring, her body taut and quivering with conflicting emotions. She was terrified; she was thrilled. She wanted the kiss to end; she wanted it to go on forever. She wanted to wrench herself out of his arms and scream at him to leave her alone; she wanted to burrow closer, to melt into him, to become a part of him, to never let him go. It was hell; it was heaven.

Through the haze of fright and pleasure, Katy became aware of Trace's hand, moving slowly, caressingly up the side of her ribcage, then halting just under her arm, the heel of his palm against the side of her breast. Pressing ever so slightly inward, his hand began to move in tiny circles, massaging the soft flesh with a sensuous rhythm.

A choked gasp was wrenched from Katy's throat as she felt her breast swell against his palm. She stiffened, and instantly Trace withdrew.

The hand was removed as he raised his head and smiled down at her. "You see. That's all it takes, my love. I'll never push you farther than you want to go."

He lowered his head and brushed a feathery kiss across her mouth, then astonished her by throwing back the covers and springing out of bed. As he walked away toward the bathroom Katy's dazed eyes roamed over the rangy frame, noting distractedly that the thin pajama bottom hanging low from his hips did little to conceal his blatant masculinity.

When the door closed behind him, Katy stared at it in perplexity. How could he just turn his emotions off at will like that? She certainly couldn't. Every inch of her body still tingled from his touch. Of course, she was grateful that he had ended the embrace before things got out of hand, she told herself quickly. It was very reassuring to know that Trace truly did intend to keep his word.

Her eyes widened as she realized that was exactly what Trace had intended. His demand that she share his bed and this morning's warm, provocative lovemaking were his method of proving to her, right at the onset, that he could, and would, keep his word.

In the bathroom the shower started, and over the rushing noise she could hear Trace singing slightly off-key. Katy slid back down under the cover, smiling to herself as the tension began to slowly seep out of her. For the first time since she had accepted Trace's proposal, she actually began to feel optimistic about their future together.

After breakfast, which, to Katy's delight, was eaten on the balcony, Trace left the choice of activities up to her. Katy elected to spend their first morning on the beach. She had never even seen an ocean before and was as excited as a child when they stepped onto the white sand of Waikiki Beach. She even forgot to be self-conscious about appearing before Trace in a bathing suit, until, slipping out of the thigh-length beach robe, she looked up to find his eyes running over her hungrily, as though he would like to devour her on the spot.

She was wearing a form-hugging maillot in a shimmering, vivid blue that exactly matched her eyes. When she had tried it on at the store it had seemed perfectly modest, but now, as she watched Trace's eyes widen and flicker with some strong emotion, Katy was very conscious of the way the clinging material molded her high breasts and boldly defined the curving line of waist and hip.

In her heightened state of awareness Katy could actually feel the touch of that hazel-green gaze as it traveled the length of her body, from the thick ebony plait that lay over one shoulder, all the way down to the pink toes curling into the sand. When he raised his eyes to hers, Katy's heart jerked to a halt, then took off with a crazy, erratic beat. The look on his face was one of such desperate longing, such intense, burning desire that she felt her mouth go suddenly dry.

"My God, you're beautiful," he groaned huskily. "Even more beautiful than I imagined."

Katy stood frozen, oblivious to the other people on the crowded beach, her gaze caught and held by the liquid green fire in his. Her lips parted, and the tip of her tongue slid over them in unconscious provocation.

Trace drew a sharp breath, took a jerky step forward, then brought himself up abruptly. Shaking his head, he heaved a sigh. His mouth twisted in a rueful smile. "Come on," he murmured hoarsely, reaching for her hand. "Let's go for a swim before I do something I'm sure I'll regret later."

In the next instant he was racing toward the surf,

dragging Katy along behind him. They hit the water at a dead run, and she squealed with shock at the coolness of it against her heated skin, but within seconds Katy felt as though she were surrounded by soft, warm silk.

Trace released her hand and they both dived into an oncoming wave. She made no attempt to keep up with him as his powerful body cleaved through the water ahead of her. Turning parallel to the beach, she swam at a leisurely pace, feeling marvelously free and relaxed. She kept at it as long as she could, but finally tired muscles forced her to stop for a rest. As she trod water Katy's eyes idly searched for Trace. When she failed to locate him she merely shrugged and flipped over onto her back.

A short while later, floating along with her eyes closed, completely lost to the world around her, Katy was brought suddenly and rudely awake when something closed around her ankle and tugged her downward. There was barely time for a short, terrified scream before the blue-green water closed over her head.

As she kicked out in blind panic her leg was released and a hard, sinewy body slid up hers. A pair of strong arms wrapped themselves around her waist, and with a powerful kick, Trace sent them both shooting upward toward the spangled sunlight.

Sputtering and gasping, they broke the surface. It took Katy several seconds to realize what had happened, but when she did her eyes shot sparks.

"Why you—you beast! You scared me half to death!" she ranted. She hit the water with the flat of her hand and sent a stinging spray into his grinning face. Trace quickly retaliated in kind, and the battle was on. With an indignant cry, Katy lunged forward and upward, coming down on his shoulders with all her weight, dunking him soundly.

For the next hour they played like two boisterous children. With mock anger, they tormented and teased one another unmercifully. It was an exhilarating new experience for Katy. Never before had she shared that kind of lighthearted fun with anyone, most especially not with a man.

Only once during their play did even a hint of sexuality break through, and that was so brief, so nonthreatening that Katy had no time to object.

Popping up suddenly in front of her, Trace had pulled her against him and planted a swift, hard kiss on her mouth. Drawing back only slightly, he traced the tip of his tongue around the outline of her parted lips.

"Mmmm, delicious," he murmured thoughtfully. "A trifle salty, but delicious all the same." He held her close for just an instant, running his hands over the wet silkiness of her body with shocking expertise. Then, with a grin, he released her and streaked away.

Bemused, Katy stared after him. She tried to work up a bit of anger, but it simply would not come. Trace in this teasing, carefree mood was impossible to resist. Slowly, a small, wicked smile curved her mouth. With a decidedly determined gleam in her eye, Katy took a deep breath and set out after him.

Finally, exhausted, they stumbled from the water and collapsed onto the woven mats Trace had placed side by side on the sand earlier.

Katy's chest was heaving from her exertions as she patted herself dry. "I can't remember ever having so much fun," she said breathlessly. Her eyes sparkling, she tossed Trace a happy smile.

He stopped his own drying to give her a long, intent look. His expression was suddenly very serious. "That was only a taste of what it's going to be like for us, sweetheart," he said in a soft, sure voice. "I'm not saying our life together will be all fun and games, but it's going to be good, babe. I promise you that. Because, whether you know it or not, we belong together, Katy."

Katy felt a fluttering, uneasy sensation begin in the

pit of her stomach. Trace's quick change of mood brought her down off the euphoric cloud with a bang. To cover her confusion, she picked up the bottle of suntan lotion and began to rub the creamy liquid methodically onto her arms and legs, letting the silence lengthen. She had no idea how to reply to his statement, so she simply said nothing.

She had finished anointing the front of her body and was about to recap the bottle when Trace took it from her.

"Roll over and I'll do your back," he instructed.

"Oh, no, I'll—"

"Don't be silly, Katy. You have very delicate skin, and I don't want to see it burned. And you needn't be afraid to let me touch you. I'm your husband. Remember?"

Reluctantly, Katy did as she was told. She felt the cool squiggle of lotion trail down her spine, then Trace's hands were moving, slowly, hypnotically over her skin. The maillot was practically backless, cut well below her waist. Trace made sure every inch of exposed flesh was covered. Katy's breathing was shallow, almost painful, as she felt the caressing touch of those calloused hands work the lotion over her shoulders and spine.

Suddenly Trace sat back on his heels and gave her a slap on the bottom. "Okay, now it's your turn."

When Katy looked up, startled, he stretched out on his stomach and handed her the bottle. "Be sure to put a lot across the top of my shoulders, will you," he instructed blithely. Ignoring her shocked expression, he rested his head on his crossed arms and closed his eyes.

Suspicion sparkled in her narrowed gaze as it ran over his bronzed form. Surely skin that deeply tanned didn't need any protection? Tight-lipped, Katy squeezed a generous mound of the white lotion into her palm and slapped it between his shoulder blades.

She had meant to keep her movements brisk and

impersonal but as her hands made contact with his flesh, she faltered. The feel of hard muscle and bone beneath warm skin was strangely pleasurable, and Katy's hands, as though with a life of their own, began to move in a slow, massaging rhythm across the broad-shouldered back, her slender fingers kneading and flexing as they smoothed on the slippery lotion.

She became mesmerized by the task. She was only dimly aware of the other supine bodies stretched out on the sand, the steady rush and retreat of the rolling waves against the shore, the dry rattle of tattered palms. Entranced, she watched the hypnotic movements of her pale fingers against the tanned skin. A few loose tendrils of hair around her face lifted in the soft breeze. The sun was warm against her bare back. She breathed in slowly, deeply, her senses swimming. All around her were the smells of sand and sea, of warm masculine flesh and coconut-scented tanning lotion.

How long she continued the sensuous massage Katy had no idea, but suddenly she realized that Trace had fallen asleep. Oddly piqued, she jerked her hands away. She recapped the bottle and stowed it in her beach bag, then stretched out beside him on her back. Her heart was thumping.

Through slitted eyes Katy watched the puffy clouds floating overhead. Honesty forced her to admit that she had enjoyed touching Trace. She hadn't expected to, but she had. What was it about Trace that made him so different from other men? Why did one man's touch evoke revulsion and fear, while another's offered pleasure and security? Was it merely a matter of technique—violent demand versus gentle enticement? Katy mulled the thought over for a moment, but finally came to the conclusion that there was more to it than that. There was something about Trace she found irresistible, something that beckoned to her, despite her attempts to ignore it.

Turning her head, she studied his strongly masculine face. Her searching gaze traced over the network of tiny lines that rayed out from the corners of his eyes, the stubby lashes that looked almost white against his bronze skin, the hard, sensual mouth that had softened appealingly in sleep. It was a surprising, disturbing thing to face, but there was no escaping it; she was strongly attracted to her husband, mentally, emotionally, and physically.

That night when she slid into bed beside Trace, Katy felt only the vaguest flutter of fear in the pit of her stomach. Surprised, she told herself she was simply too exhausted to be afraid.

They had spent the entire afternoon sightseeing, beginning with a walking tour of Chinatown and the Cultural Plaza. Amazed and delighted by the wide variety of wares, Katy had gone from shop to shop, looking at rare pottery, turquoise, jade, silks, and herbs. In one of the food shops she had stared in wide-eyed amazement when shown one of the greatest of Chinese delicacies—an egg which was a century old and which looked and smelled every single year of it.

After Chinatown came a quick visit to the Falls of Clyde, the world's only surviving one-hundred-year-old, full-rigged, four-masted sailing ship. From there they toured the State Capitol building and the Iolani Palace, where the last two Hawaiian monarchs had lived.

That evening they had enjoyed dinner and a spectacular Polynesian show in the hotel dining room.

Now, feeling pleasantly tired and sleepy, Katy couldn't summon up the strength to resist when Trace gathered her into his arms and pulled her close.

With her head resting on his arm he placed his other hand under her chin and tilted her face up. "Tired?" he questioned, chuckling softly as he met her drowsy look.

"Mmmmmm."

"Happy?"

Surprise widened her eyes. She frowned as she considered the question for a moment, then a slow smile curved her mouth. "Yes," she admitted, with a discernible trace of astonishment in her voice.

Trace dropped a soft kiss on her mouth, then pulled back and smiled. Tenderly, his fingers stroked the silky black strands at her temple. "Good. I want you to be happy."

All the love he felt was clearly visible in his eyes, in his strong-boned, handsome face, and Katy reacted to it instinctively. Feeling warm and cherished cuddled against Trace's hard strength, her body weak with a delicious languor, she had no defense against the powerful attraction that drew her to him. Without thinking, she lifted her hand and stroked his cheek, smiling sleepily.

Trace drew in a sharp breath, then his head swooped. He kissed her long and hungrily, with a tender passion that made her heart swell in her chest until it nearly suffocated her. By gradual degrees the kiss grew stronger, deeper, more demanding. He parted her lips with ease and slid his tongue into the sweet moistness of her mouth, rubbing it against hers in a rough, sensuous caress.

Katy felt feverish, her body trembling from the strange erotic sensations pulsing through her. The soft, exquisitely sensual kiss seemed to penetrate to her very soul. A small nagging voice in the back of her brain told her to push him away, but she didn't have the strength or the will.

Trace abandoned her mouth to bury his face in the curve of her neck, nibbling at the sensitive skin. Katy's senses were alive with pleasure as she docilely gave herself up to the passionate embrace.

The large hand at her waist began to move slowly

upward, but this time, instead of resting against the side of her breast, it cupped the warm soft mound possessively.

When Katy stiffened, the hand stilled instantly, but did not release its prize. For long moments the only sound in the room was the harsh rasp of their disturbed breathing. At last, when she made no further protest, Trace began to caress her, tentatively at first, then growing gradually bolder. Katy closed her eyes and held her breath as her nipple puckered into a hard bud of desire. A soft moan escaped her tight throat.

Encouraged by her passive acceptance, Trace reclaimed her lips with a scorching demand, his tongue probing relentlessly into the intimate recesses of her mouth, while his hand slid downward. Katy's stomach muscles clenched as his flattened hand spread out over her quivering abdomen, edging steadily downward, moving in slow circles.

When the caress threatened to become unbearably intimate, Katy wrenched free of the drugging kiss and grabbed his wrist. "No, Trace. Don't," she cried in panic.

Rolling over onto his back, Trace pulled her close and gently stroked her arm and the side of her face. His breathing was ragged and the heavy thunder of his heart roared in her ear. "Don't worry, sweetheart. Everything is fine," he assured her in a soft, crooning voice.

Katy shivered against him as Trace repeated the soothing caress over and over, with infinite care and patience. When at last her breathing returned to normal and she relaxed against him, he placed a warm kiss on her forehead. "Good night, darling."

Long after sleep had claimed Trace, Katy lay staring into the darkness. Two days ago, if anyone had told her that she would allow Trace the liberties he had taken tonight she would have told him he was crazy. Yet, she had not only allowed them—she had enjoyed them.

And that scared her more than anything. That her own body could betray her came as a definite shock. She had been so *sure* of her invincibility.

Sighing, Katy snuggled her head more firmly against Trace's shoulder and determinedly closed her eyes. She was simply too exhausted to worry about it now.

Chapter Nine

To Katy's amazement, the honeymoon she had dreaded turned into the most thoroughly enjoyable two weeks she had ever known. Each day in the Pacific paradise brought a wonderful new experience, and somehow, Trace's stimulating, yet undemanding companionship seemed to increase her pleasure.

When they weren't sailing or snorkeling or just lazing on the beach, they went shopping or sightseeing. One morning they took the tour boat out to the Arizona Memorial in Pearl Harbor, and from there visited the Punchbowl, the huge crater known as the Cemetery of the Pacific. Both came away from the sobering sights deeply affected. To shake off the somber mood, Trace took Katy to a charming, open-air restaurant on the beach, where they ate lunch amid the throbbing pagan beat of Polynesian music. Afterward they spent a leisurely afternoon wandering through the Bishop Museum.

Though at first put off by the rather forbidding appearance of the Victorian stone building's armory-like exterior, Katy was soon delighted as she viewed the amazing collection of treasures housed inside, especially the huge whale hanging from the ceiling in Hawaiian Hall.

There were artifacts of tortoiseshell, whalebone, and beautifully carved wood in striking contrast to the ornate thrones of the Hawaiian monarchy. But most impressive of all to Katy were the priceless red and yellow feather cloaks and capes once worn by Hawaiian chiefs.

"Oh, Trace. Aren't they gorgeous," she breathed ecstatically, when they stopped in front of the first display. "Just look at those colors. They haven't faded a bit, even after all these years."

"Very impressive," Trace agreed. "But then, they ought to be. Those things were handmade from feathers of exotic birds which are now extinct. And since each bird produced only one feather that was considered brilliant enough for a chief's garment, it took years just to complete one robe."

"How do you know that?"

"Oh, I read it somewhere," he said with an air of off-handed superiority. Then his eyes twinkled. "I think it was in one of those brochures the hotel provides."

"Oh, you!" Katy gave him a sharp poke in the ribs. "And there I was, all set to be impressed with your vast store of knowledge."

Laughing, Trace flung his arm around her shoulders and led her toward the next display.

The casual embrace was something he did often. No matter where they were or what they were doing, he always managed to touch her in some way. If his arm wasn't draped across her shoulders or hooked around her waist, his hand was tunneled under the heavy fall of ebony hair and curved around her nape, his fingers absently massaging the tight muscles.

At first the constant contact made Katy nervous, but after a few days she became resigned to it. By the end of the first week, the feel of his arm around her seemed the most natural thing in the world.

They spent several days driving around the island,

exploring remote beaches, visiting extinct volcanoes, orchid nurseries, and pineapple and sugar plantations. On one of their trips they stopped to picnic at Makaha, better known as Surfer's Paradise, and watched in awe as muscled young men on surfboards rode the forty-foot waves in to shore.

Every evening they ate at a different restaurant in order to sample the wide variety of ethnic cuisine the islands offered. After dinner they either enjoyed Honolulu's fantastic nightlife or went for long walks on the beach. Rarely did they return to their suite before midnight. But no matter how late the hour, each night when they relaxed in the king-sized bed, Trace gathered Katy into his arms and made gentle, persuasive love to her.

Knowing that she had only to give the slightest sign of resistance and Trace would stop, Katy did not panic when his caresses gradually became more and more intimate. By the end of their stay, though she still had no intention of allowing him to consummate the marriage, Katy could no longer deny that she enjoyed Trace's lovemaking.

On the morning of their departure, while Trace had gone down to the lobby to settle their bill, Katy gathered up their last minute articles and added them to the cases she had packed the night before. She took one last look around the suite for anything she may have missed, then closed the cases and snapped the locks shut.

Restless, with nothing more to keep her occupied, she slid open the glass door and stepped out onto the balcony. Her eyes were sad as she leaned against the railing and gazed down at the beach. At this early hour there were only a few heads bobbing in the blue water.

Katy sighed. How she hated to leave. Their stay had been ideal—a period out of time when the problems facing them seemed far removed. As she thought back over the last two weeks, a small, self-derisive smile tugged at her mouth. Well, it had been ideal from her point of view at any rate. She doubted that Trace would describe their rather unorthodox honeymoon in quite the same way.

But in any case, it was over now and reality was about to intrude. Katy had the uneasy feeling that it was going to be much more difficult to keep her husband at arm's length once they returned to the farm.

The soft swish of the sliding door alerted her to Trace's presence, and Katy cast a quick glance over her shoulder. A wan smile of greeting flickered over her face before her gaze returned to the horizon.

"Feeling sad about leaving?" Trace asked perceptively. Stepping up behind her, he slid his arms around her waist and pulled her back against him, resting his chin on the top of her head.

The blue of sky and ocean merged into a wavy blur as her eyes suddenly welled with tears. "I guess so," she replied in a wavering voice. Katy swallowed hard on the lump that rose in her throat. Good Lord! Why was she behaving so emotionally? Anyone would think she was a starry-eyed bride who couldn't bear for her honeymoon to end!

A low rumble of laughter vibrated against her back. "Well, as much as I'd love to just stay here and enjoy the lotus-eating life with you, I'm afraid I have a horse farm to run." Trace bent his head and pressed a feathery kiss against her temple. "But don't worry, sweetheart, we'll come back someday. In fact, I'll make you a promise right now that we'll return on our twenty-fifth anniversary for a second honeymoon."

Katy turned within the circle of his arms and gave him a troubled look. "Oh, Trace. Do you honestly believe—"

A sharp rap on the door cut her off and drew an impatient look from Trace.

"That'll be the bellhop."

Katy stared after him as he stepped back into the

sitting room, her expression thoughtful. What were the chances of a platonic marriage surviving twenty-five years? Practically nil, she admitted to herself sadly. Especially when the husband was a passionate and virile man like Trace.

Refusing to dwell on the tight knot of pain that twisted her stomach, Katy glanced at the ocean one last time, then resolutely stepped inside.

Her father was waiting for them at the Tyler airport when they arrived that evening. The despondent mood that had clung to her all day disappeared like a wisp of smoke at the first sight of his craggy face. When he grinned and opened his arms wide, Katy flung herself into them.

"Oh, Dad, I'm so glad to see you!" she cried as he lifted her off the floor.

"And it's glad I am to be seein' you, Katy darlin'," Tom replied huskily. For a moment he hugged her tightly against his chest, as though he could not bear to let her go, the big hand spread across her back patting her with rough tenderness. When he finally put her on her feet, he held her at arm's length. Tom's face beamed as he noted the healthy, sun-kissed skin and the happy sparkle in her blue eyes. "Well now. I'm thinkin' marriage agrees with you, Katy girl. You're more beautiful than ever."

His gaze went beyond her to the man who stood waiting. The look on Tom's face spoke of admiration, respect, and fondness, but most of all, of a deep, profound gratitude. Releasing Katy, he stepped forward and held out his hand. "Welcome home, Trace," he said warmly.

"Thanks, Tom. It's good to be back."

All the way to the baggage claim section the two men talked business. Katy walked along between them, smiling contentedly. Her spirits seemed to rise a little with each step. Suddenly it felt very good to be home.

When Trace left them to claim the luggage, Tom turned to his daughter with a questioning look. "Well, now. Tell me, Katy girl, was I right to trust that young man?"

A faint twinge of pink swept over Katy's face. Her father had never once doubted Trace's integrity. "Yes, Dad. You were right. Trace is a man of his word, just as you claimed all along. I'm sorry I ever doubted you or him."

"Don't worry about that, sweetheart. You had a perfect right to be apprehensive. The important thing is you're learning to trust him. That's absolutely essential if you're going to have a good marriage." Tom smiled gently and patted her arm. "Give him a chance, Katy girl. He loves you very much. He'll make you happy, if you'll let him."

Katy's answering smile was wan. What did that mean? Did he want her to accept Trace as a husband, in the fullest sense of the word? Even knowing what he did?

He was watching her intently, as though waiting for her reply, but Katy didn't know what to say. Her feelings for Trace had altered during the past two weeks. But not *that* much.

Glancing over her father's shoulder, she was relieved to see that Trace had recovered their luggage and was striding toward them. He had a bag in each hand and two more under his arms. His powerful body showed no sign of being burdened by the load, but Tom quickly relieved him of two of the cases.

"I'm parked right outside," he said, nodding his head toward the exit doors. "We'll just load these into the trunk and be on our way. I'll have you home in two shakes."

"Good," Trace replied, smiling warmly at Katy. "I'm anxious to get home and carry my bride over the threshold."

Surprise widened Katy's eyes for just an instant. For

a brief time she had forgotten that she would now be living in the big house. In the weeks prior to the wedding the problem of where they would live had seemed very minor, compared to all the other things that had been worrying her. Now it seemed to loom very large. The thought of living in the huge, pillared mansion filled her with apprehension. Katy wasn't at all sure she was capable of taking Saundra's place as mistress of Green Meadows. Or that she even wanted to.

Tom was already walking toward the door and Trace moved to follow him. Two steps away he stopped and turned back to Katy, a questioning look on his face. "Coming, sweetheart?"

After the briefest of hesitations, Katy nodded and picked up the two tote bags full of souvenirs which sat at her feet. With one in each hand and a stiff smile on her face, she took the few steps that brought her level with her husband. Side by side, they walked across the crowded lobby and stepped out into the warm Texas night.

All of Katy's fears soon proved groundless. Within a month she had settled into the big house and her role as its mistress as though she had been born to it.

She had expected the house to be a constant reminder of Henry and Saundra, but Trace, with the sensitivity she was coming to expect from him, eliminated that problem almost immediately. The morning after their arrival he took her on a tour of the house. Very tactfully he pointed out the furnishings which had been in his family for years, especially those items that had belonged to his mother. The rest, he explained tersely, had been selected by Saundra.

After viewing only a few rooms Katy could easily spot which was which. Evelyn Barnett had chosen elegant period pieces with clean, classic lines, while Saundra's taste ran more to the ornate.

Halfway through the tour Trace surprised her by saying, "I want you to redo the house to suit yourself, Katy. You can have a free hand to change anything you want, in any way you want. My only demand is that you get rid of every item that belonged to Saundra. I want that woman's presence obliterated from our home just as soon as possible."

"Oh, Trace, I couldn't do that!" Katy protested quickly. "The house is lovely, just as it is!"

"That may be, but I think a house should reflect the taste of its mistress." He lifted her chin with one finger and smiled into her anxious face. "I keep remembering how warm and inviting your father's cottage is. There's a wonderful, homey feeling there that this place lacks. I like that, Katy. I like it very much. And I think you do too."

A wry smile twisted one corner of her mouth. "Well, yes. Actually, I do. But I somehow can't imagine this house with homemade braided rugs and chintz-covered furniture."

"Maybe not. But I'm sure that whatever you choose will be perfect. Keep anything of Mother's that appeals to you, but get rid of Saundra's. Then just let yourself go."

Katy continued to resist the idea for a time, but in the end, Trace was adamant. Once started, she tackled the project with enthusiasm, spending countless hours looking at furniture catalogues, paint samples, and upholstery and drapery swatches. In some rooms she made sweeping changes, in others only small ones, which, nevertheless, managed to subtly alter the tone of the decor. Within a few weeks the house had begun to take on a new personality.

Much to everyone's surprise, Katy returned to her job at the daycare center. It was what she wanted to do, and Trace didn't mind. Mattie certainly didn't need her help caring for the house.

Gradually her life settled into a pleasant routine. The

days were spent helping Jane with the throng of irrepressible but delightful children. The evenings were spent quietly with Trace. Several times a week Trace persuaded her father to join them for dinner, and Katy was deeply touched by the thoughtful gesture. The fact that her husband and her father liked and respected one another filled her with a deep sense of contentment.

Katy knew that to others they appeared to be the typical newlywed couple. Trace certainly made no effort to hide the fact that he adored his wife, and Katy would have been less than human had she not responded to the constant attention he showered on her. When he looked at her in that special way, or simply touched her gently in passing, she felt warm all over. All of her doubts about Trace vanished under his consistent, loving care.

As the weeks passed Katy began to realize that she was happier than she had ever been in her life. If there were times when she felt a twinge of regret at the look of hungry yearning she often glimpsed in Trace's eyes, or when her own body stirred with restless longings, she quickly suppressed the feelings. She didn't want anything to disturb the even tenor of their relationship.

For a long time it looked as though nothing would. Then one night, about two months after their return from Hawaii, she arrived home to find Trace packing.

Katy froze in the bedroom doorway and stared at the open case spread out on the bed. A cold feeling of dread clutched at her. Her frantic gaze went to Trace, where he stood bent over an open dresser drawer.

"Where are you going?" she asked bluntly, her voice breathless with anxiety.

Surprise and pleasure lit Trace's handsome features when he swung around. "Hi, darling. I didn't hear you come in." Carelessly tossing a stack of clean underclothes into the open case as he passed the bed, he crossed the room and took her into his arms, kissing her long and lingeringly on the mouth.

Normally Katy melted under the soft persuasion of his kiss, but tonight she stood rigid within his arms, her lips cold and unresponsive. All that registered on her mind was that half-filled case. The moment he released her, her eyes went back to it. "Where are you going?" she repeated urgently.

"I'm leaving early tomorrow morning for California. I received a call from Ed Tillman this afternoon. You remember him—the California rancher who was here a few weeks ago looking over some thoroughbred stock? Well, it seems he's finally made up his mind. He's buying the black stallion and six mares, and he wanted me to deliver them to his ranch just as soon as I can."

"I see," she said quietly. "And how long do you think you'll be gone?"

"Oh, about ten days, I'd say. I'm going to take it slowly, and stop often to exercise the horses. Their legs tend to swell on long hauls like this, and I want them to be in top shape when we arrive, so I'll probably take four or five days to make the trip. Then I'll have to stay a few days to make sure they settle in okay. I should be back by a week from Friday. But don't worry if it takes a bit longer."

"Do you have to go? Why can't you send someone else?"

"Normally I would. But Ed is very influential among California's horse set, and this is the first time he has bought any of our stock. I want to be sure everything goes well."

Ten days. She wouldn't see him for ten days. Katy felt her stomach plunge as though she had suddenly swallowed a ten pound rock. Distressed by her reaction, she pulled out of his arms and walked briskly over to the open case.

"My goodness, just look at this mess." Her voice

came out high and unsteady, sounding nothing at all like her. "I don't understand why you men are so helpless when it comes to something like packing. None of this will be fit to wear by the time you get to California." Shaking her head, she pulled the jumble of clothing from the case and began to refold it. "Why don't you just get out whatever else you want to take, and I'll pack it for you."

"I was hoping you'd say that," Trace said, chuckling.

Katy kept her head down as she carefully repacked each item, blinking rapidly to fight back the threatening tears. She was furious with herself. Why should she mind that Trace would be gone for almost two weeks? Or that he hadn't asked her to go? Only a few months ago she would have been relieved. So she had gotten used to spending her evenings with him. So what? It wasn't the end of the world. There was no reason for her to be lonely just because Trace wouldn't be here for a few days. She could spend every evening with her father. The way she used to. She probably wouldn't even notice that he was gone.

As Katy put in the last item and straightened up she felt Trace's hands slide around her waist from behind, as his lips nuzzled aside her hair and nibbled at her neck.

Katy relaxed against him, and for just a moment, reflected irrelevantly on how easily she had grown accustomed to his touch.

"You know, honey, I've been thinking. It's about time we gave a party, and this would be a good time for you to plan it—while I'm gone and out of your hair."

"A party? Why do we have to give a party?"

Trace turned her slowly and locked his hands in the small of her back. There was a devilish gleam in his eyes and his mouth was twitching. Katy leaned back against his arms and eyed him suspiciously.

"Well, it's the custom around these parts for newly-weds to give some sign to their family and friends that they're ready to leave the bedroom and rejoin the rest of the world," he stated with a perfectly straight face, then laughed aloud as Katy blushed furiously. "Surely you've noticed that we haven't had any visitors or received any invitations since we returned? They're all waiting for us to indicate that we wouldn't be averse to a little socializing. A party would accomplish that."

Her face still warm, Katy stared at the top button on his shirt. "What kind of party?" she asked with a decided lack of enthusiasm. She hated the very thought of giving a party. The last one they'd had ended in disaster.

"Oh, just something casual. Maybe a barbecue around the pool. And don't worry, we won't invite too many people. After dinner tonight I'll make up a list of the ones I feel we should ask, and you can add anyone else you want. Mattie can help you with the food and decorations. She's an old hand at this sort of thing. Plan it for two weeks from Saturday. I'm sure to be back by then." He tilted his head to one side and gave her a slow, coaxing smile. "Okay?"

Resentment smoldered in Katy's blue eyes as she stared back at him, but there was no resisting Trace when he turned on the charm. Finally she released a long, resigned sigh and nodded. "Okay."

Katy turned her head and glanced at the illuminated dial of the bedside clock. One fifteen. With a disgusted sigh she threw back the covers and slipped out of bed. The silken folds of her nightgown fluttered soundlessly around her ankles as she walked barefoot across the carpet to the window. Drawing back the lacy curtains, Katy stared morosely out into the darkness.

Moonlight filtered through the huge oak tree by the drive, casting a dappled pattern of light and shadows across the manicured lawn. From behind the house, hidden in the dense forest, came the incessant, high-pitched hum of a thousand nameless insects. A movement caught her eyes, and as Katy watched, a small furry animal scampered across the grass and disappeared into the shrubbery.

The quiet was nerve-wracking. Katy shifted restlessly and stared up at the black velvet sky.

This was the fourth night in a row that she hadn't been able to sleep. And she knew why. The simple truth of the matter was that she missed Trace. Dreadfully.

She had grown accustomed to falling asleep in his arms, with the sound of his strong heartbeat beneath her ear and the warm comfort of his hard body pressed against hers. Without him that enormous bed was just a cold empty space.

And it wasn't only at night that she felt this grinding loneliness. She missed him every minute of the day, even during those times, like at work, when she normally didn't see him. Since the moment he had disappeared down the drive, pulling that long stock trailer full of horses behind his truck, she had walked around feeling as though her heart were encased in lead. And she hadn't been in the least successful in hiding her feelings. Jane had noticed her unhappiness only that morning. In her usual, forthright manner, she had gotten right to the heart of the problem.

"Sweetie, if you don't like the pattern on these dishes, just say so and I'll buy some new ones. There's no need to scrub it off."

It took several seconds for Jane's voice to penetrate, but finally Katy turned her head and gave her friend a blank look, her blue eyes slightly out of focus. "What?"

"You've been washing that same plate for the last five minutes," Jane explained with exasperated amusement.

"Oh! I'm sorry. My mind must have been wandering." Hastily, Katy swished the dish through the rinse water and placed it in the rack.

"Your mind isn't wandering, doll, it's taken a hike.

You've been off in some world of your own for the past three days. What's the matter? Did you have a fight with that dreamy man you married?"

Katy pulled the plug in the sink and watched the water whirlpool down the drain. "No, of course not. Anyway, that would be a bit difficult, since he left Tuesday morning to deliver some Thoroughbreds to a rancher in California."

"Ah-ha! Now the light dawns!" Jane crowed in triumph. "I knew it had something to do with Trace. For two months you've been absolutely glowing with happiness. Now, all of a sudden, the light has gone out of you and you're walking around like a zombie." She cocked her head to one side and narrowed her eyes shrewdly. "You're missing that man like hell, aren't you?"

"No—yes—I mean . . ." Katy's stammered denial trailed away to nothing in the face of Jane's smug grin. Sighing heavily, she walked to the couch and sank down in one corner, her shoulders drooping. Her eyes remained fixed on her plucking fingers as they toyed absently with a loose thread in the upholstered arm. She sent up a prayer that one of the kids would wake up and give her an excuse to escape. There wasn't a hope in hell that Jane would just let the matter drop.

Katy risked a quick glance at her friend, then wished she hadn't. Jane was still standing there with her hands on her hips, watching her with that I-dare-you-to-deny-it smirk on her face.

"Oh, all right. You win. So maybe I do miss him a little," Katy admitted grudgingly. "We've been married over two months now and . . . and"—she paused and shrugged—"we've become friends and I'm used to having him around. That's all."

"Horse feathers!" Jane snorted succinctly. "When a friend goes on a trip you say 'so long, Charlie' and go on about your business. Only when you're in love do you count the days until a man returns."

A high-pitched wail from the nursery drew Jane toward the door. With her hand on the knob, she stopped and looked back at Katy's stunned face. "Think about it, Katy," she said softly.

Well, she'd thought about it all right. With a sigh, Katy let the lacy panel fall back into place and turned toward the lonely bed. Since Jane had made that astounding observation she had thought of nothing else.

And slowly, relentlessly, the truth had forced its way to the surface. She was in love with Trace.

Katy stretched out full length on the bed and stared through the darkness at the ceiling. How had it happened? When had she lost her fear of Trace? In two months' time she had gone from lying in his arms like a slab of granite, to the point where she could not sleep without him by her side.

Looking back on the past two months, Katy realized there had been no one occasion that had marked the change in their relationship; it had been a gradual process. With infinite care and patience, Trace had shown her repeatedly that she could trust him. As that trust had grown, her fear had receded. Those horror-filled moments in the woods would probably always haunt her to some extent, but she knew now that she could no longer equate Trace's touch with the vile, unspeakable things those two men had tried to do to her. There was not even the vaguest similarity between their violent lust and her husband's tender, passionate love.

Once her fear had been conquered, it had been impossible to hold in check the powerful attraction that had always existed between them. Each night, when Trace held her in his arms, it became more and more difficult for her to pull away before their lovemaking reached its ultimate conclusion. Her body ached for the fulfillment only Trace could give.

A delicious shiver raced through Katy's body as she

recalled the heart-stopping sensations Trace could so easily arouse in her. With a look or touch he could turn her bones to water. When he held her and kissed her as though he would draw her into his very soul, nothing else in the world mattered.

Yet, for a while, Katy had stubbornly refused to admit that the attraction between them was anything more than physical. It was easier that way. Physical attraction could be denied fulfillment; love could not.

But she could no longer ignore her feelings. It had taken only these few days apart for her to realize that without him she was miserable. What was it Trace had said? When you find that one right person it's like finding your other half? Katy smiled. He was certainly right about that.

Rolling onto her side, Katy buried her face in Trace's pillow, then groaned. Mattie had changed the sheets that morning and the clean linens smelled only of soap and the freshness of outdoors. Now even Trace's scent was missing.

Her longing for him had reached an intensity that was painful. As she lay there staring into the darkness, feeling sick with need, Katy made the most momentous, most difficult decision of her life. It could no longer be avoided or postponed. When Trace returned she would let him know that she loved him, and that she was ready for their marriage to be a real one. *How* she would do it, she hadn't the slightest idea. She couldn't quite see herself just walking up to him and blurting it out.

With a sigh, Katy hugged his pillow against her chest. Somehow she'd find a way. They couldn't go on like this.

Chapter Ten

Late in the afternoon on the day Trace was due to return, Katy stood at the kitchen sink, deftly peeling potatoes. Every few seconds her restless gaze darted out the window toward the stables. He would have to go there first to unhitch the horse trailer, she knew. The thought of seeing Trace again made Katy almost faint with excitement.

Her eagerness had made her haunt the kitchen all day, since the windows in that room afforded the best view of the stables and back road. After about her tenth visit, Mattie had finally become so exasperated over finding her underfoot constantly that she had tied an apron around Katy's waist and put her to work. Katy didn't mind. She was grateful for an excuse to stay.

As she reached for another potato, Katy's eyes were drawn irresistibly to the window once again. The familiar blue truck was just rolling to a stop beside the stables. Her heart gave a little leap and the potato peeler clattered into the sink. Katy stood frozen for a moment, then her feet were carrying her toward the back door. En route the apron was snatched off and tossed over the back of a chair. Oblivious to Mattie's knowing grin, she pushed open the screen door and loped down the back steps two at a time.

Katy's heart was pounding with anticipation as she started across the yard. With each step she was walking faster and faster, until by the time she was halfway there she was running.

Trace was just rounding the front of the truck as Katy approached the stables. Catching sight of him, she was suddenly overcome by a fit of intense shyness and skidded to a halt several feet away.

Trace spotted her at the same moment and stopped too, his eyes flaring like dry kindling. "Katy." Her name came out on a breathless sigh. Katy wasn't even sure she'd heard it.

They stood absolutely still, staring at one another. An expectant silence hung in the air between them.

For the past week Katy had planned exactly what she was going to say, exactly how she was going to behave when Trace returned. Now, every carefully rehearsed word flitted right out of her mind. Her brain simply refused to function.

The hazel-green eyes made a quick, avid search of her face and figure. Surprise flickered in their depths as he noted her heaving chest and flushed cheeks. Then, slowly, a devastating smile curved his mouth, and he broke the tense silence with a husky, "Hello, Katy."

Katy stared back at him with wide, hungry eyes. His sandy hair was windblown into an attractive disarray. The chambray work shirt, stretched taut across his hard, muscled chest and broad shoulders, seemed to emphasize his primitive masculine appeal. His loose-jointed stance was deceptively casual, but his eyes were alert as he watched Katy's silent struggle.

Her insides were fluttering like snowflakes in a storm. The desire to touch him was so strong it was almost irresistible, but her feet seemed to be rooted to the spot. She couldn't force a sound through her aching throat.

From the corner of her eye she saw her father emerge from the stables. Taking in the situation at a glance, he stopped short and placed his hands on his hips. "For heaven's sake, Katy girl!" his gruff voice chided. "What are you waiting for? Give the man a proper welcome."

Katy's uncertain gaze went from Trace to her father, then back. The look in the hazel eyes echoed Tom's words, and when Trace opened his arms wide she obeyed the command. With a joyful cry, she sped across the intervening space and flung herself against his chest.

She was lifted clear off the ground as their lips met in a long, burning kiss. His arms crushed her so tightly that Katy could barely breathe, but she didn't care. Winding her arms around his neck, she thrust her hands into his hair and pulled him closer.

Katy's uninhibited response seemed to release a floodgate in Trace. He kissed her with all the pent-up need of a man long denied, the fierce, driving hunger of the past months surging to the surface. Katy responded instinctively, glorying in the possessive, passionate demand.

Finally, the initial torrent spent, the kiss gentled into a long, exquisitely tender exploration that left them both weak and trembling. When at last their clinging lips parted, Trace allowed her body to slide downward until her feet touched the ground. His arms remained around her, holding her close, as he buried his face in the silky fall of her hair.

"Oh, sweetheart, I've missed you like hell," he muttered raggedly against her neck, breathing in the very essence of her. "But, dear heaven! It was worth every lonely hour just to have you greet me like this."

Katy smiled as she snuggled deeper into his arms. His shirt was unbuttoned halfway to his waist. Without conscious thought, she wound her arms tightly around his lean middle and pressed her face against his chest. A delicious shudder rippled through her as she buried her nose in the cloud of curling hair and inhaled deeply of his masculine scent. Trace's arms tightened, and Katy closed her eyes, utterly content. This was where she belonged.

The truck engine roaring into sudden life jolted them back to their surroundings. Surprised, they turned to find Tom beaming down at them from the pickup's cab.

"Don't mind me," he drawled. "I'm just going to take the trailer down to the barn and clean it out." With a casual wave, he put the truck in gear and drove away, the empty horse trailer bouncing and rattling along behind.

The knowing twinkle in her father's eyes had brought a flush to Katy's face but Trace didn't seem in the least disconcerted. Smiling that crooked little half smile that made her stomach flutter, he drew her close and fitted her tightly against his side. With his arm curved around her shoulders and hers around his waist, they turned and walked toward the house.

Later that night, as she sat before her dressing table, mercilessly dragging a brush through her hair while she waited for Trace to emerge from the bathroom, Katy was as taut as a drawn bow.

It was one thing to decide, with the safety of hundreds of miles between them, that the time had come to make their marriage a real one. Following through on the decision was something else again. She loved Trace. She had no doubts about that. And her body pulsed with a deep, burning need that only his complete possession could satisfy. Yet fear, insidious, mind-choking fear, was slowly twining its curling tendrils through her.

It wasn't a fear of Trace; she knew that he would never hurt her. It was a fear of the unknown. Giving yourself completely over to another person, experiencing the ultimate intimacy, was something Katy had never even contemplated until a week ago.

The sudden opening of the bathroom door brought an end to her self-torment. Katy's heart kicked painfully against her ribs as she watched Trace's mirrored image become inexorably larger.

He was clad in only a towel, which draped low from his hips. The sculptured beauty of his chest and shoulders made Katy's pulse race. In the soft light from the bedside lamp his naked skin glowed like polished bronze, its smooth surface broken only by the V-shaped pattern of burnished gold chest hairs.

Purposefully, relentlessly, his intent gaze never once leaving her, he moved across the lush carpet. When he came to a halt, only a few inches separated them.

A shiver rippled through Katy as their eyes met in the mirror and his hands settled warmly on her bare shoulders. She inhaled the intoxicating mixture of pine soap and clean male scent that emanated from him. Through the thin silk of her gown she could feel the heat of his body all across her back.

There was no mistaking the message in his eyes. Trace had not misread the silent invitation in her uninhibited greeting, in the hungry looks she had given him all through dinner.

"Let's go to bed, Katy,' he whispered with husky sensuality. "I want to hold you."

For a painful few seconds Katy's lungs refused to function. Then, mesmerized by the burning look in those deep-set eyes, drawn by a need even stronger than the curling fear in the pit of her stomach, she allowed him to lift her from the stool and lead her, trembling and silent, to the bed.

The light covering was thrown back, and as Katy slid obediently into the enormous bed, the lamp was clicked off. There was a soft plop as the towel hit the carpet, then the mattress tilted under Trace's weight. Powerful, sinewy arms reached out and gathered her close, molding her intimately against the hard, masculine body, his naked flesh burning its imprint into her through the silk gown.

"Oh, Katy, Katy. I feel as though I've waited all my

life for this," Trace breathed against her lips just before his mouth claimed them.

The kiss was both passionate and tender, demanding and entreating, and Katy's lips blossomed under it like a bud unfurling beneath the sun. A soft moan escaped her as he explored the silken sweetness of her mouth with excruciating sensuality. She felt his tongue tracing her lips, delicately probing the sensitive membranes on the inside of her cheek. Trace had kissed her passionately many times but always before there had been that element of restraint, of rigid control. No more. He made no effort to curb his desire, and under the questing kiss, Katy felt her own control slipping, the last remnant of doubt and fear fading into oblivion.

"Oh, God, how I love you," he murmured thickly as his mouth trailed across her cheek. Katy was beyond reply, her body shivering deliciously as his tongue traced the convoluted swirls of her ear. His broad hand ceased its rhythmic caress of her hip to glide slowly upward. It paused briefly at the indented curve of her waist, then again to cup the warm fullness of her breast, before moving, with sure determination, to her shoulder. One at a time, the thin straps of her gown were moved aside, and the slippery material was lowered to her waist.

He drew back to look at her. Moonlight filtered through the lacy curtains at the window. In its dim, silvery glow his eyes burned feverishly.

"Beautiful. You're so beautiful."

His hand curved possessively around one breast, his fingers stroking softly over the curving slope.

Then Katy gasped and her mind went spinning out of control as his lips captured the rosy tip and tugged gently. Her flesh responded instantly, forming a hard bud of desire, achingly tight and tender.

Palm flat, fingers extended, his hand moved onto her quivering stomach, and instinctively Katy's body arched upward, liquid heat surging through her veins.

Her hands moved restlessly over the corded muscles in his neck and shoulders. "Trace. Oh, Trace," she moaned softly, lost to everything but the driving need that pulsed through her.

"I know, sweetheart. I know."

Abandoning her breasts, his mouth forged a moist trail upward, pausing on the way to delicately trace her collarbone and nibble at the underside of her jaw. Katy was caught in the exquisite rapture of the slow, tantalizing caress, and she waited breathlessly for his mouth to reclaim hers.

It was a few seconds before she realized that his hands had stilled, the softly spoken love words had ceased. Through the haze of passion clouding her vision Katy saw that Trace had pulled away and, propped on one elbow, was looking down at her expectantly. Heavy lidded eyes blinked once, twice, but he continued to watch her in that intent way, as though waiting for an answer to some unspoken question. Or had it been unspoken?

"Wha—what . . ."

"Tell me what you want, Katy," Trace urged in a low whisper. "I have to know, for both our sakes."

Confusion clouded her expression for a moment, then, slowly, the meaning of his words sank in, and her eyes widened. Trace wanted her to *ask* for his lovemaking!

Shock rippled through her. She couldn't! She simply couldn't!

But, looking into his face, Katy knew, with sickening certainty, that if she wanted a real marriage, she must. From the very beginning Trace had put the burden of decision on her, and he wasn't going to relieve her of it now. There would be no claims of coercion or seduction or misunderstanding later. If she wanted her husband, she would have to tell him so.

Gathering her courage, Katy swallowed hard and tried to force the words through her constricted throat, but they simply would not come. The inhibitions of a lifetime were just too strong. Feeling her happiness slipping away, Katy gazed back at him in mute desperation, tears welling up in her eyes.

Abruptly, Trace rolled away from her. Moving to the edge of the bed, he sat hunched over, elbows on knees, his head cradled in his hands.

Something about the rigidity of his back, the utter, absolute defeat in every line of his body, sent a chill through Katy. A panicky fear, worse than any she had ever known, began to build inside her, and she reached out to touch him.

"Trace, I . . ."

Violently, he jerked away.

"For God's sake, Katy, don't touch me! My control does have its limits!"

Flinching from the stinging lash of his angry voice, Katy drew back and huddled motionless against the pillows.

Trace reached out and flicked on the bedside lamp. Lifting a hand, he raked it through his hair, rumpling it even more than Katy's fingers had.

"I'm sorry, Katy. I didn't mean to snap. None of this is your fault," he said in a flat, dejected tone. Grim-lipped, he clasped his hands together between his knees and shot her a brooding look over his shoulder. "You tried to warn me that this might happen, but, arrogant fool that I am, I was positive I could make it work. I love you so much that I thought all I had to do was show you and give you time, and eventually you'd come to me. Tonight, when you seemed so happy to see me, I assumed . . . Oh, hell! What difference does it make now."

Snatching up his robe from the end of the bed, he slid it over his shoulders and stood up. Katy felt cold and sick inside as she watched him walk away toward the dressing room. At the door he stopped and turned back to her with an odd, defeated smile on his lips. "I think, under the circumstances, I'd better sleep in the dressing room. No matter what the future holds for us, I don't want to break my word to you, and I'm afraid my control has been stretched to its outer limits. Good night, Katy."

The door clicked shut behind him, and Katy lay frozen. Why had she lain there like a statue? Why hadn't she found the courage from somewhere to tell him what he wanted to hear? Instead, by her silence she confirmed his mistaken assumption that she didn't love him or want him.

Turning her face into the pillow, Katy let the thick down muffle her sobs. She wept long and bitterly, her shoulders shaking as the terrible, wrenching cries tore from her throat, until finally the emotional storm was spent and she was drained.

Hours later she still lay, dry-eyed, staring at the ceiling, her emotions in utter turmoil. Like a swinging pendulum, her anger switched from herself to Trace, then back again. Couldn't he see, by her greeting, by the way she responded to his slightest touch, that she was his, totally? Why did he insist that she put her feelings and desires into words? That was asking too much. Couldn't he *see* that?

She sighed deeply. No. No, it wasn't asking too much. Trace had told her from the beginning how it was going to be. She just hadn't realized he meant it quite so literally. Or, more to the point, she had never truly expected the situation to arise.

She was a fool. A blind, stupid fool. For almost two weeks she had yearned desperately for him, had practically counted the hours until she could lie in his arms and know his love. Now, here they were on his first night home, in separate beds.

The dressing room door drew her longing gaze repeatedly. She had only to knock on that door and utter a few simple words and all the barriers would be gone. Yet she couldn't.

Chapter Eleven

Standing on the patio, among the group of gaily dressed, laughing people, Katy was filled with a strange sense of unreality. That she could smile and talk, or even function at all, after the miserable week she had just endured, seemed something of a miracle.

Taking a sip of her drink, she let her eyes wander. Like a homing device, her gaze automatically sought out and zeroed in on Trace. He was with a group of people on the other side of the pool, his back to her. How symbolic, Katy mused bitterly.

The pain that followed that thought almost made her cry out. Determinedly, she jerked her gaze away. This was neither the time nor the place to indulge in a fit of self-pity. Tonight marked her debut as mistress of Green Meadows, and pride, if nothing else, demanded that she give a good accounting of herself. Mentally squaring her shoulders, Katy exchanged her watery drink for a fresh one, pasted a stiff smile on her face, and started toward the nearest cluster of people.

Somehow she managed to carry out her duties as a hostess. Moving from one group to the next, she made introductions, saw that everyone had a drink, and exchanged inane small talk, not one word of which she could recall five minutes later. And through it all she was vitally aware of Trace and the fact that he seemed deliberately to be keeping a careful distance between them.

And that, much to her dismay, was exactly what he had been doing for the past week. Katy had expected, or at least hoped, that Trace would return to their bed, once passions had cooled and they had both recovered from that debacle of a reunion. It had not happened. Trace still slept in the dressing room, while night after night she tossed and turned alone in that huge bed, sick with unhappiness and the steadily building fear that she was losing him.

On the surface nothing had changed. As always, Trace treated her with great care and consideration and was unfailingly pleasant. Yet there was a subtle difference in their relationship. There were no more warm, teasing looks, no more gentle bantering conversations, and worst of all, no more attempts at lovemaking. Trace hadn't so much as touched her, even accidentally, since the night he returned from California. They were polite strangers, occupying the same house.

Katy knew the situation could not continue for long. The strain was intolerable. Aware also that the solution to the problem lay in her own hands, she was consumed with guilt and self-disgust.

Dozens of times during the past week she had steeled herself to face him and tell him exactly how she felt. But each time her courage had failed her at the last moment. It was maddening! She wanted to tell him. Knew it was what he wanted to hear. But she just couldn't!

Katy absently twirled the ice cubes in her drink and pretended to listen as Trudy Bledsoe described her teenage son's latest football injury in great detail. Trudy was the wife of one of Trace's old college buddies. Even listening with only half an ear, Katy had already learned that Trudy's whole life revolved around her husband, John, and their three children. In a sudden fit of self-torment, Katy idly wondered if she would be around long enough to become friends with the talkative, but otherwise pleasant, woman.

From across the pool, Trace's deep laughter rang out, drawing Katy's gaze like a magnet. Her mouth tightened when she saw the way a willowy blonde was clinging to his arm as though she couldn't stand without his support. Katy turned away sharply, and when Trudy paused to draw a breath she quickly excused herself, saying that she wanted to speak with Mattie about serving dinner.

Once inside the house, Katy ignored the kitchen and went directly upstairs to the master bedroom. In the adjoining bath she rummaged through the medicine cabinet for the aspirin, and finding them, downed a couple with a glass of water. After two hours of watching that woman drape herself all over Trace, the dull ache in her temples had become a full-fledged tension headache.

The moment she arrived Monica Traverse had thrown her arms around Trace and kissed him full on the lips. Much to Katy's chagrin, he hadn't objected in the least. When the long, passionate embrace was over, Trace had laughingly disentangled the woman's arms and told her to behave herself. Then, without the slightest hint of embarrassment, he had turned to Katy and introduced her as his cousin, a relationship which the lovely Monica had quickly discounted as having no importance.

"Fourth cousins, darling," she had drawled seductively. "That hardly constitutes next of kin. Anyway, our relationship has always been more in the 'kissing cousin' category, wouldn't you say?" Giving him a heavy-lidded look that spoke volumes, she smiled slowly and purred, "Don't tell me you've forgotten all those long summer afternoons we spent in the hayloft?"

The sly innuendo sparked an instant reaction in Katy. Anger, hot and strong, surged through her, and for the first time in her life, she felt an urge to commit physical violence. The dislike she had felt for Saundra was nothing compared to the hostility this woman aroused. Hayloft indeed!

But if she found Monica's remark offensive, Trace certainly didn't. Throwing his head back, he let out a bark of delighted laughter.

"You little devil. You haven't changed a bit, have you? Stirring up trouble is obviously still your favorite pastime." Trace grinned at the blonde in a way that made Katy's heart lurch painfully. "Well, this time it won't work, sweetheart. My wife isn't in the least jealous. Now, mind your manners and say hello to Katy."

"Hello, Katy," Monica parroted, smiling archly as her green eyes swept over Katy in a quick, head to toe inspection. "I really should hate you, you know, for stealing this gorgeous man the minute my back was turned. If I hadn't been touring Europe this summer, you would never have gotten away with it."

Ignoring Katy's startled expression, Monica slipped her hand through Trace's arm and gave him a reproachful look. "And I really shouldn't even speak to you, you naughty man. How *could* you marry someone else, when you know I've been lusting after you for years? I'm heartbroken!"

"Maybe I just got tired of waiting to catch you between husbands," Trace teased.

"Oh, you! Just for that I'm not going to let you out of my sight all evening."

And she hadn't either, Katy reflected grimly.

She tried to tell herself she had nothing to fear. After all, Trace loved her. He had proven that in a thousand different ways. But still a niggling doubt persisted in the back of her mind. She kept remembering that when she had pointed out to Trace the possibility that the marriage might never be consummated, he had told her that was his problem. He hadn't, however, explained how he would deal with it. The mere thought that he might have the marriage annulled, or take a mistress, made Katy sick at heart.

Giving herself time to regroup her forces, she sank onto the bench in front of the dressing table and began to brush her hair with slow, soothing strokes. Then she swept it back high over her temples and secured it with two amethyst-studded combs. After she had touched up her lipgloss, Katy stood and surveyed her reflection. She adjusted the full sleeves of her gauzy, burgundy blouse and tucked it more securely into the waistband of the long, matching skirt. Then, with no further excuse to delay, she made her way back downstairs to the party.

When Katy stepped outside, she discovered that during her absence a space had been cleared at one end of the patio for dancing, and Trace and his "kissing cousin" were now wrapped in each other's arms, swaying to the slow, seductive music that poured from the outdoor stereo speaker.

The tightness in Katy's chest increased. Pivoting on her heel, she stalked back into the kitchen and informed Mattie, rather curtly, that it was time to serve dinner.

"Who's the blond bombshell?" Jane asked her a short time later, when Katy joined the Cawleys at one of the tables scattered around the back lawn.

Katy didn't need to ask who she was talking about. Her eyes went immediately to the table where Trace and Monica were seated, and her set expression became even stiffer. The woman was practically sitting in his lap!

"That's Monica Traverse, Trace's cousin," she replied, striving for indifference, then completely spoiling the effect by adding, "she's been in Europe for the last six months and now she's making up for lost time."

"She certainly is," Jane agreed heartily, not even bothering to comment on Katy's incensed tone. "And if I were you, my girl, I'd put a stop to it. Pronto!"

"What am I supposed to do, threaten to scratch her eyes out if she doesn't back off? I'm sure Trace's snooty relatives would *love* that. I get the distinct impression they're all just waiting for me to make some horrible social blunder."

"Well, you'd better do something, sweetie, because that woman has got the hots for your husband. And if he decides to take what she's so obviously offering, you won't have anyone but yourself to blame."

Frank's scandalized "Jane!" had no effect at all.

"I mean it!" his wife continued pugnaciously. "It's time Katy realized that she's married to a passionate, virile man, and if she continues to keep him at arm's length she's going to lose him."

Katy didn't need Jane to tell her something she already knew. The same worrisome thought had been running through the back of her mind all week, like some blurred, flickering film. Tonight's little episode merely brought it into sharper focus.

Eyes fixed on her plate, she listlessly poked at the savory barbecue with her fork, and murmured, "I know."

The wavering note in Katy's voice brought Jane's head around with a snap. After a search of her face she quickly changed the subject.

The meal seemed interminable. Seated not more than ten feet away from Trace, Katy couldn't miss the provocative gleam in Monica's eyes whenever she looked at him or the way she seemed to be plastered against his side. Every time the woman's husky laughter rang out, Katy's jaw clenched tighter. By the end of the meal her teeth were aching.

Later, when Trace and his cousin returned to the improvised dance floor, and the woman literally melted against him, Katy watched through narrowed eyes and

indulged in a delightful fantasy in which she shoved
Monica, fully clothed, into the deep end of the pool.

Katy was slow to anger. She could count on the
fingers of one hand the number of times she had truly
lost her temper. But that was not to say she didn't have
one. When pushed long enough, and far enough, she
could explode into a magnificent fury that was all the
more shocking for its rarity. An evening of watching
Trace accept the cloying attentions of another woman,
while virtually ignoring his wife, had her doing a slow
burn. By the time the party began to break up, she was
nearing flash point.

Predictably, Monica was the last to leave. Katy had
just closed the front door after saying good night to her
father and the Cawleys when Trace strolled into the
entrance hall with the woman clinging to his arm.

"I'm going to walk Monica to her car, darling," he
announced in a casual tone that set Katy's hackles up.
"I won't be but a minute—why don't you go on up to
bed. Mattie and the others just about have everything
cleaned up, and I know you're tired."

His solicitude grated on Katy's nerves like a finger-
nail scraping on a chalk board, but her blistering glare
was wasted. His attention had already returned to the
woman at his side.

"It was a lovely party, Katy," Monica cooed. "I can't
remember when I've had such a good time."

It was all Katy could do to restrain herself. Gritting
her teeth, she barely managed a tight, "Thank you,"
before pivoting on her heel and stalking up the stairs. If
Trace thought her behavior rude, that was just too bad!
At that moment polite platitudes were beyond her.

Katy marched into the master bedroom and, in a
very childish, but totally satisfying fit of temper,
slammed the door with a force that rattled the pictures
on the wall. Seething, she began to pace the room.
Every time she passed the bedside table her eyes went
to the clock. How long did it take to say good night, for

heaven's sake! Imagination stoked the fire of her jealous anger, and with every tick of the clock the pressure built higher. Twenty minutes later, when Trace strolled into the room, she was ready to let fly.

He stopped just a few feet inside the door and stretched, flexing his broad shoulders and giving vent to a huge yawn. "Boy, am I bushed," he commented lazily. Releasing a long sigh, he gave Katy a friendly smile and headed for the dressing room, absently unbuttoning his shirt on the way. "All things considered, it was a nice party, don't you think?" he tossed over his shoulder.

He didn't seem to notice that Katy had jerked to a halt at his entrance, or that she now stood in the middle of the room, still fully clothed, glaring daggers at him.

"Oh, just terrific!"

Trace had taken two more steps before he caught the snapping sarcasm in her voice. Faltering to a stop just as he reached the dressing room door, he turned slowly and shot her a quizzical look. The beginnings of a puzzled frown creased his forehead.

Too incensed to say another word, Katy swung away and stalked to the dressing table, where she angrily snatched the combs from her hair, flung them into a drawer and slammed it shut. She then went to work on the amethyst earrings.

Trace's frown deepened.

"Did you enjoy the party?" he asked, more cautiously this time.

Her lips tightened as she met his gaze in the mirror. "Enjoy it? I just spent six hours talking to a group of people I didn't know, while my husband completely ignored me. And you want to know if I *enjoyed* it?"

"I'm sorry if you feel that I ignored you, Katy, but as the host I had an obligation to entertain our guests. We both did." Pulling his unbuttoned shirt from his trousers, he let it hang free while he stood, hands on hips, watching her intently, his expression wary.

"Entertain the guests? Is that what you were doing?" She spun on one heel and stormed across the room, coming to a halt just inches from him, her eyes shooting blue flames as she glowered up into his surprised face. "As far as I could see the only person you bothered to entertain was 'cousin Monica,'" she sneered, while angrily working open the buttons on her long sleeves. Without waiting for a reply, she turned and stalked back across the room.

Trace's brows jerked upward, and his expression froze. Then, slowly, noting her stiff, angry movements, his features began to relax. Amused satisfaction glittered in his eyes as he said, coaxingly, "Now, come on, Katy. Be fair. I circulated among the guests all evening. I'm quite certain I talked to everyone, at least twice."

"Yes! And the whole time you had that woman plastered to your side!" she snapped, ripping the blouse off over her head. She flung it into a chair beside the bed and retraced her steps. "And speaking of time, just why did it take twenty minutes to say good night when you walked your dear cousin to her car?" she demanded, poking his bare chest with one slender finger.

"Monica wanted to talk to me about something. I guess time just got away from us."

"Talk to you! *Talk* to you! She had all evening to talk to you!" Katy railed. "Although I will admit, talking wasn't what she seemed to have on her mind. That woman was all over you, and I didn't see you objecting. Not once!" The finger jabbed again. "Well, let me tell you something, Trace Barnett. I will not be treated that way. While you were playing footsie with Monica I spent a ghastly evening deflecting pitying looks from your friends and trying to ignore the knowing smirks your uppity relatives cast my way. It was humiliating! And I don't intend to put up with it. That woman is not to set foot in this house again! Is that clear?"

Whirling around, she marched back to the bed, kicked off her shoes and wiggled out of the burgundy skirt and matching half slip, nearly sizzling with fury. With a careless toss, both garments joined the blouse in the chair. Head held high, she stalked to the dresser and removed a clean nightgown.

"Come on, Katy," Trace said, chuckling. "Monica doesn't mean anything to me. For heaven's sake! We grew up together."

Katy threw her nightgown on the bed, incensed by the so-called explanation. She faced him with her fists planted on her hips, eyes blazing, oblivious to the fact that she was clad in only a scanty, lace and silk, burgundy teddy, which revealed a great deal more than it concealed. She was much too furious to give a thought to her state of undress.

"Oh, I've heard all about the way you grew up together," she snarled. Pelvis thrust forward, hips swaying provocatively, she sauntered up to Trace in an exaggerated imitation of Monica's seductive slink.

Trace's eyes roamed avidly over her scantily covered body, a flame leaping in their depths as they studied the milky gleam of her breasts, where they strained against their sheer, lacy confinement.

Giving him a sultry, feline look, Katy mimicked huskily, "Don't you remember all those long summer afternoons in the hayloft, darling?"

Her face hardened. Abandoning her seductive pose, Katy threw her head back and glared at him, her lip curling in disgust. "Grew up fast, didn't you."

Trace's mouth quivered suspiciously. With studied nonchalance, he stripped off the shirt and tossed it at the hamper behind him. Then, crossing his arms over his chest, he leaned a bare shoulder against the door frame. "Keep that up and you're going to wear a rut in the carpet," he said, addressing the words to her retreating form as she stomped back toward the bed.

If Katy heard the remark she chose to ignore it. She was much too caught up in her satisfying tirade to be sidetracked. It felt wonderful, absolutely marvelous, to spew out all the anger that had been boiling up inside her for hours, and she wasn't about to deny herself the pleasure.

"Now you just listen to me," she continued pugnaciously, as she fumbled with the ribbon ties that held the bodice of the teddy together. "If you think I'm going to put up with you carrying on with that woman, or *any* woman, you can just think again. I won't stand for it! You forced your way into my life, refused to take no for an answer, and practically bludgeoned me into marriage. Well, you got what you wanted, Trace, and now you're stuck with me. There will be no other women in your life *or* your bed. I'm . . ."

A choked sound behind her brought her whirling around, the unfastened teddy falling open to below her waist. Her jaw dropped at the sight of Trace, struggling manfully to contain his laughter.

"Don't you *dare* laugh at me, Trace Barnett!" she shrilled at him, stamping her foot in outrage.

Caught red-handed, unable to hold it in any longer, Trace threw back his head and let the sputtering chuckles blossom into rich, full-bodied laughter, a warm, exultant sound of pure joy.

"Trace, you stop that right now or I'll—I'll—"

Her irate threat succeeded in choking off his laughter, but did nothing to dim his euphoric joy. Bristling with indignation, but too stunned to move, Katy watched with open-mouthed astonishment as Trace strolled toward her with a ridiculously happy grin splitting his face.

"Oh, Katy, Katy. You're such an adorable little goose."

Frowning, she plucked at the hands that settled on her waist. "I'm *not* adorable and I'm *not* a goose," she retorted testily. "Now, let me go! And stop grinning like an idiot!"

The hands at her waist tightened and Katy's feet suddenly left the floor. Frantically, she clutched at

Trace's shoulders as he whirled her around in circles. When he finally stopped her head was spinning.

Still holding her aloft, he grinned triumphantly. "Ahhh, but you are *very* adorable, my darling. Especially when you're in a flaming rage and haven't the faintest idea why."

"Haven't the fa . . ."

That was too much! Fists doubled, Katy rained blows on his head and shoulders. "Put me down! Put me down this instant!" she shrieked.

"Of course, my love." Grinning, Trace tossed her onto the bed. In a blink he followed her down and pinned her to the mattress with his body, his mouth closing over hers in burning possession.

Katy writhed beneath him. She was determined to fight the instant pleasure his touch evoked. Squirming and pitching, she tried to evade his insistent mouth, but Trace did not let up until, at last, she quieted.

Then, slowly, cautiously, he lifted his head and stared down at her. A gentle smile curved his mouth but his eyes were quite serious.

"Now, as much as I'm intrigued by the sleeping tigress I somehow accidentally let loose, I want you to calm down and tell me, in plain, straightforward language, what it is you really want. I think we both know, but I want you to say it anyway."

Katy glared back at him, her expression a mixture of pride and defiant anger. When she remained stubbornly quiet Trace gave her a little nudge.

"Come on, Katy. Say it."

"All right, dammit! I love you! And I want you!" she snapped in a completely unlover-like tone. "Is that what you wanted to hear?"

Trace sucked in a deep breath and closed his eyes. He remained perfectly still for a moment, as though in the grip of some agonizing pain. Then, slowly, he relaxed, and on a heart-felt sigh, breathed, "At last."

With exquisite tenderness, he lowered his head and kissed her again, his lips tasting, coaxing, caressing. Katy felt all the fight go out of her, and with a moaning sigh of surrender, she wrapped her arms around him and held him close, returning the delicately passionate kiss with an eagerness that instantly brought a growling response from Trace.

They touched and tasted, exploring each other with sensuous delight, reveling in the new freedom. In mere minutes Trace had shed his remaining clothes and the ridiculous wisp of silk and lace was smoothed from Katy's body.

His lips and tongue played over her, kissing and tugging at her breasts, stroking the silky, quivering skin of her belly. Katy returned the caress, shyly at first, then with growing sureness, her heart swelling as she felt his shuddering response.

The driving urgency of their need for one another could not be restrained for long. When neither could bear the exquisite torture any longer, Trace rose over her. Hesitating, he looked down into her flushed face.

"Are you very sure, Katy?" he asked, with a vulnerability that tugged at her heartstrings.

A tremulous smile curved her mouth as she took his face between her palms and pulled his head down. Against his lips she whispered, "Love me, Trace."

He took her gently, guiding her through that first, fleeting moment of discomfort with tender care, then, passion blossoming freely, they moved into a realm Katy had never even dreamed of. Together they climbed higher and higher, until the almost unbearable pleasure reached its peak and exploded in a showerburst of ecstasy. In the shuddering aftermath, they clung to one another and drifted slowly down to earth, spent and utterly replete.

"Did I hurt you, darling?" Trace asked some time later.

Katy nuzzled her nose against the side of his neck, a soft smile tugging at the corners of her mouth as she caught the thread of concern in his voice. "Only a little. But it was worth it." Her arm tightened on his waist. "Oh, darling, I had no idea it would be like that. I feel so foolish, putting both of us through all that torment for so long."

Trace tipped her chin up and smiled lovingly at her contrite expression. "Don't worry about it, sweetheart. It was something you had to work through. I've always wanted you. I don't deny that. But I wanted you free of fear, and loving me as much as I love you." Cupping the side of her face, he stroked her bottom lip with his thumb, while his eyes ran over her wonderingly. "I swear to you, Katy, it's never been like that with anyone else. Never."

"And it never will be," she retorted spiritedly. "Because I warn you right now, you've landed yourself a very jealous wife, like it or not."

Trace laughed delightedly and hugged her close. "Oh, I like it, I like it. But I must admit I'm still in shock. I had no idea my sweet, gentle Katy had such a fiery temper."

"I do when provoked," she informed him with a stern, narrow-eyed look. "And if 'cousin' Monica gets within ten feet of you again she'll find herself on the receiving end of it."

"Calm down, spitfire. Monica is a nuisance but you have no reason to be jealous of her. She simply likes to stir up trouble, then sit back and watch the fur fly." He gave her a devilish look. "Though I will admit, had I known the effect she would have on you I would have invited her over long ago. She accomplished in a few hours what I haven't been able to do in months. But for the record, no matter what she implied, Monica and I have never been lovers." He planted a quick kiss on her mouth and grinned. "Satisfied?"

"I'll be satisfied as long as you love me," Katy whispered.

Rolling her over onto her back, Trace framed her face between his hands and stared intently into her eyes, his own burning. Katy's heart turned over at the love she saw there. "That will be forever," he promised huskily.

Silhouette Romance

IT'S YOUR OWN SPECIAL TIME
Contemporary romances for today's women.
Each month, six very special love stories will be yours
from SILHOUETTE.

$1.75 each

☐ 100 Stanford	☐ 127 Roberts	☐ 155 Hampson	☐ 182 Clay
☐ 101 Hardy	☐ 128 Hampson	☐ 156 Sawyer	☐ 183 Stanley
☐ 102 Hastings	☐ 129 Converse	☐ 157 Vitek	☐ 184 Hardy
☐ 103 Cork	☐ 130 Hardy	☐ 158 Reynolds	☐ 185 Hampson
☐ 104 Vitek	☐ 131 Stanford	☐ 159 Tracy	☐ 186 Howard
☐ 105 Eden	☐ 132 Wisdom	☐ 160 Hampson	☐ 187 Scott
☐ 106 Dailey	☐ 133 Rowe	☐ 161 Trent	☐ 188 Cork
☐ 107 Bright	☐ 134 Charles	☐ 162 Ashby	☐ 189 Stephens
☐ 108 Hampson	☐ 135 Logan	☐ 163 Roberts	☐ 190 Hampson
☐ 109 Vernon	☐ 136 Hampson	☐ 164 Browning	☐ 191 Browning
☐ 110 Trent	☐ 137 Hunter	☐ 165 Young	☐ 192 John
☐ 111 South	☐ 138 Wilson	☐ 166 Wisdom	☐ 193 Trent
☐ 112 Stanford	☐ 139 Vitek	☐ 167 Hunter	☐ 194 Barry
☐ 113 Browning	☐ 140 Erskine	☐ 168 Carr	☐ 195 Dailey
☐ 114 Michaels	☐ 142 Browning	☐ 169 Scott	☐ 196 Hampson
☐ 115 John	☐ 143 Roberts	☐ 170 Ripy	☐ 197 Summers
☐ 116 Lindley	☐ 144 Goforth	☐ 171 Hill	☐ 198 Hunter
☐ 117 Scott	☐ 145 Hope	☐ 172 Browning	☐ 199 Roberts
☐ 118 Dailey	☐ 146 Michaels	☐ 173 Camp	☐ 200 Lloyd
☐ 119 Hampson	☐ 147 Hampson	☐ 174 Sinclair	☐ 201 Starr
☐ 120 Carroll	☐ 148 Cork	☐ 175 Jarrett	☐ 202 Hampson
☐ 121 Langan	☐ 149 Saunders	☐ 176 Vitek	☐ 203 Browning
☐ 122 Scofield	☐ 150 Major	☐ 177 Dailey	☐ 204 Carroll
☐ 123 Sinclair	☐ 151 Hampson	☐ 178 Hampson	☐ 205 Maxam
☐ 124 Beckman	☐ 152 Halston	☐ 179 Beckman	☐ 206 Manning
☐ 125 Bright	☐ 153 Dailey	☐ 180 Roberts	☐ 207 Windham
☐ 126 St. George	☐ 154 Beckman	☐ 181 Terrill	

IT'S YOUR OWN SPECIAL TIME

Contemporary romances for today's women.
Each month, six very special love stories will be yours
from SILHOUETTE. Look for them wherever books are sold
or order now from the coupon below.

$1.95 each

☐ 208 Halston	☐ 228 King	☐ 248 St. George	☐ 268 Hunter
☐ 209 LaDame	☐ 229 Thornton	☐ 249 Scofield	☐ 269 Smith
☐ 210 Eden	☐ 230 Stevens	☐ 250 Hampson	☐ 270 Camp
☐ 211 Walters	☐ 231 Dailey	☐ 251 Wilson	☐ 271 Allison
☐ 212 Young	☐ 232 Hampson	☐ 252 Roberts	☐ 272 Forrest
☐ 213 Dailey	☐ 233 Vernon	☐ 253 James	☐ 273 Beckman
☐ 214 Hampson	☐ 234 Smith	☐ 254 Palmer	☐ 274 Roberts
☐ 215 Roberts	☐ 235 James	☐ 255 Smith	☐ 275 Browning
☐ 216 Saunders	☐ 236 Maxam	☐ 256 Hampson	☐ 276 Vernon
☐ 217 Vitek	☐ 237 Wilson	☐ 257 Hunter	☐ 277 Wilson
☐ 218 Hunter	☐ 238 Cork	☐ 258 Ashby	☐ 278 Hunter
☐ 219 Cork	☐ 239 McKay	☐ 259 English	☐ 279 Ashby
☐ 220 Hampson	☐ 240 Hunter	☐ 260 Martin	☐ 280 Roberts
☐ 221 Browning	☐ 241 Wisdom	☐ 261 Saunders	☐ 281 Lovan
☐ 222 Carroll	☐ 242 Brooke	☐ 262 John	☐ 282 Halldorson
☐ 223 Summers	☐ 243 Saunders	☐ 263 Wilson	☐ 283 Payne
☐ 224 Langan	☐ 244 Sinclair	☐ 264 Vine	☐ 284 Young
☐ 225 St. George	☐ 245 Trent	☐ 265 Adams	☐ 285 Gray
☐ 226 Hamson	☐ 246 Carroll	☐ 266 Trent	
☐ 227 Beckman	☐ 247 Halldorson	☐ 267 Chase	

SILHOUETTE BOOKS, Department SB/1

1230 Avenue of the Americas
New York, NY 10020

Please send me the books I have checked above. I am enclosing $_____
(please add 75¢ to cover postage and handling. NYS and NYC residents please
add appropriate sales tax). Send check or money order—no cash or C.O.D.'s
please. Allow six weeks for delivery.

NAME _____

ADDRESS _____

CITY _____ STATE/ZIP _____

Let Silhouette Inspirations show you a world of Christian love and romance... for 15 days, free.

If you want to read wholesome love stories...with characters whose spiritual values are as meaningful as yours...then you'll want to read Silhouette Inspirations™ novels. You'll experience all of love's conflicts and pleasures—and the joy of happy endings—with people who share your beliefs and goals.

These books are written by Christian authors...Arlene James, Patti Beckman, Debbie Macomber, and more...for Christian readers. Each 192-page volume gives you tender romance with a message of hope and faith...and of course, a happy ending.

We think you'll be so delighted with Silhouette Inspirations, you won't want to miss a single one! We'd like to send you 2 books each month, as soon as they are published, through our Home Subscription Service. Look them over for 15 days, free. If you enjoy them as much as we think you will, pay the enclosed invoice. If not, simply return them and owe nothing.

A world of Christian love and spirituality is waiting for you...in the pages of Silhouette Inspirations novels. Return the coupon today!

Silhouette Inspirations Home Subscription Service
120 Brighton Road, P.O. Box 5020, Clifton, NJ 07015

Yes, I'd like to receive two new Silhouette Inspirations each month as soon as they are published. The books are mine to examine for 15 days, free. If I decide to keep the books, I will pay only $2.25 each, a total of $4.50. If not delighted, I can return them and owe nothing. There is never a charge for this convenient home delivery—no postage, handling, or any other hidden charges. *I understand there is no minimum number of books I must buy, and that I can cancel this arrangement at any time.*

☐ Mrs. ☐ Miss ☐ Ms. ☐ Mr.   BCR3P4

Name	(please print)	
Address		Apt. #
City	State	Zip
Area Code	Telephone Number	

Signature (If under 18, parent or guardian must sign.)

This offer, limited to one per household, expires September 30, 1984. Terms and prices are subject to change. Your enrollment is subject to acceptance by Simon & Schuster Enterprises.

SILHOUETTE INSPIRATIONS is a trademark and service mark of Simon & Schuster, Inc.

Silhouette Romance

Coming Next Month

The Man From the Past by Dorothy Cork

Ferris never dreamed that the dark, compelling cousin of the man she once loved would be the one to conquer her heart. Now Cleve proposed a marriage of convenience to save her beloved winery. But Ferris longed for a marriage in every sense of the word.

Permanent Fixture by Janet Joyce

Megan knew that her new job as executive secretary to the president would be a challenge. But she didn't think she'd have to fight her attraction for her new boss—especially when Brandon Scott let her know just how personal he expected his personal secretary to be.

Chance of a Lifetime by Joan Smith

Handsome John Balfour was number one on the Millionaire Eligible Bachelor List of Kim Monk's roommate. But Kim loved John for himself, not his wealth—how could she convince him she was nothing like her friend?

Partners in Love by Jean Saunders

Robin Pollard's promise to be Luke Burgess' assistant seemed like a terrible mistake. The rugged stranger not only wanted to develop the wild Cornish landscape she loved, but it seemed he had plans for Robin as well . . . plans she didn't think she could resist.

Rain on the Wind by Elizabeth Hunter

Pippa had been too unhappy with her deceitful husband to ever marry again. But Joel was determined to initiate her into the delights of love she had missed the first time, and Pippa was strangely vulnerable to this blond giant's slanted smile.

The Singing Stone by Rena McKay

Jordan Kyle seemed to be exactly the kind of man Jennifer's mother had warned her against: a sun-bronzed maverick who specialized in women on a two week holiday. But could it be that he really was the tender man Jennifer thought she glimpsed behind the glorious mask?